GEORGE B. CRESSEY

No geographer has seen as much of Asia, or has written so meaningfully of that continent as Prof. Cressey. He has lived in Asia off and on during two decades, for a total of eight years, and his travels exceed 100,000 miles. His first trip to Tibet was on foot and required 109 days from Peiping; on his latest journey to China he flew via the Atlantic and Africa in a week.

Three visits have taken him to 10 of the 16 Soviet Republics. The first was in 1923 when he crossed Siberia to enter China via Mongolia. The second was in 1937 when he was a delegate to the International Geological Congress and remained to serve as Consultant to the Great Soviet World Atlas and later to travel in the Siberian Arctic with the Northern Sea Route Administration. In 1944 he had the rare opportunity of visiting Soviet Middle Asia with some time in Tashkent, Samarkand, and Bukhara. These professional trips have included familiarity with scores of mines and factories, and with pioneering developments in agriculture.

While in China, Prof. Cressey taught for six years at the University of Shanghai. He is familiar with all of the 28 provinces and has also undertaken field work in Mongolia and Tibet. In 1934 he served as Consultant to the National Agricultural Research Bureau of the Chinese government, and in 1943-44 was Visiting Professor under the Division of Cultural Cooperation of the U. S. Department of State.

In addition, Dr. Cressey has travelled in India from the Khyber Pass to Cape Comorin; has been in Japan on three occasions, and has also visited Java and the Philippines.

Professor Cressey is a graduate of Denison University and holds a doctorate in geology from Chicago and another in geography from Clark. From 1931 to 1945 he was Chairman of the Department of Geology and Geography at Syracuse University, and has been appointed Visiting Professor at Stanford University for 1945-46. He has lectured at the Summer Sessions of Harvard, Western Reserve, Michigan and Columbia Universities. During the war he served as Consultant to the Department of State, the Board of Economic Warfare, and Military Intelligence. He is widely known as a lecturer.

The Basis of
Soviet Strength

STUDIES ON THE GEOGRAPHY OF ASIA

BY GEORGE B. CRESSEY

THE ORDOS DESERT OF INNER MONGOLIA

Denison University Bulletin, 1933

CHINA'S GEOGRAPHIC FOUNDATIONS

McGraw-Hill Book Company
Published in 1934, sixth impression 1944
Published in French as Géographie Humaine et
Économique de la Chine, Paris: Payot, 1939

PIONEERING IN YENISEILAND

Denison University Bulletin, 1939

ASIA'S LANDS AND PEOPLES

Whittlesey House
Published in 1944, fourth impression 1945
Spanish translation by Editorial Sudamericana, S.A.,
Buenos Aires, in preparation, and Chinese translation
by The Commercial Press, Chungking, in preparation

THE BASIS OF SOVIET STRENGTH

Whittlesey House, 1945

When the Soviets developed their steel industry under the five-year plans, they utilized the latest machinery from the Western World. This rolling mill is at Zaporozhe in the Ukraine. (*Sovfoto*)

The basis of Soviet strength lies in her dynamic people and in the abundant resources of their land. (*Paris Exposition, 1937*)

The Basis of
Soviet Strength

BY

GEORGE B. CRESSEY

CHAIRMAN, DEPARTMENT OF
GEOLOGY AND GEOGRAPHY
SYRACUSE UNIVERSITY

New York Whittlesey House *London*

MC GRAW-HILL BOOK COMPANY, INC.

1 9 4 5

FOURTH PRINTING

*The quality of the materials used in the manufacture
of this book is governed by continued postwar shortages.*

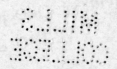

PUBLISHED BY WHITTLESEY HOUSE
A division of the McGraw-Hill Book Company, Inc.

Printed in the United States of America

A PERSONAL FOREWORD

THIS book has grown out of three visits to the Soviet Union. When I first crossed the country in 1923, the effects of the Revolution and its civil disorder were still obvious. Many buildings in Moscow retained bullet marks, the cobblestone streets in Leningrad were in bad repair, and people were living in acute distress. The night before I entered the country I had dinner with a person who advised me not to step off the train or outside my hotel as the chances were good that I would be waylaid and lose at least my pocketbook if not my head. Siberia was bleak.

In 1937 I was one of the American delegates to the Seventeenth International Geological Congress held that year in Moscow. This provided exceptional opportunities to see some of the achievements of the five-year plans. Following the meetings I spent a month in Siberia on one of the Congress excursions, and later returned for another month as a guest of the Northern Sea Route Administration. While in the Soviet Union I also served as consultant to the Great Soviet World Atlas. No one could study the U.S.S.R. in 1937 without being deeply impressed with the ability of the government to meet great objectives, and with the pioneering spirit of the people.

It was in 1944 that I again visited the country, this time to cross Soviet Middle Asia, with some time in Tashkent, Samarkand, Bukhara, and Baku. Almost my first reaction as I crossed the border was "Here is a country where people smile." The war had brought many shortages to civilians, but their spirit was high.

· v ·

A Personal Foreword

When I returned to the United States after my second visit I often prefaced my remarks by saying that I was merely presenting a factual report so that people might bring their prejudices up to date. The events of the war have made such a comment inappropriate. No longer can Americans afford to remain ignorant about one of the world's major powers. The Soviet Union has demonstrated her right to respect and understanding; as one of her allies we can no longer permit our judgment to be influenced by prejudice either of the left or of the right.

A considerable part of this book originally appeared in "Asia's Lands and Peoples," but it has been extensively re-written and new chapters have been added. All the pictures are new.

I am particularly indebted to the Smithsonian Institution for permission to make extensive use of their bulletin on The Peoples of the Soviet Union by Dr. Aleš Hrdlička.

GEORGE B. CRESSEY

Syracuse University
March 1945

READER'S GUIDE

Those who wish to quickly secure the highlights of this book without going into geology or anthropology are advised to examine the maps and pictures, and to read the following sections.

CONTENTS

Contents

LIST OF MAPS

The Basis of
Soviet Strength

ONE-SIXTH OF THE EARTH

THE SOVIET REALM

IN ALL the world there is no other country quite like the Soviet Union. Here is the most striking social and political experiment of our times. Regardless of whether we favor or oppose socialist ideology, the Union of Soviet Socialist Republics challenges our attention.

This volume is not a presentation of political theory, nor does it attempt to evaluate the cultural well-being of the people of the Union. Rather it is a consideration of those environmental and human factors which lie behind the country's achievements and provide the basis for Soviet strength. No citizen of today's world can afford to remain in ignorance about the geography of this area.

Within the U.S.S.R. lies one-sixth of the land on earth. From the Baltic to the Pacific these eight million square miles spread across 160° of longitude, nearly halfway around the globe. Whereas the longest great-circle distances in the United States are under 3,000 miles, the opposite corners of the Union are over 5,000 miles apart. Transferred to the Western Hemisphere, Leningrad would lie just south of Nome, Alaska, while eastern Siberia would touch Norway.

Here too live nearly one-tenth of the world's people, the most cosmopolitan group of nationalities in any single country. Nowhere is there a more patriotic or enthusiastic group of citizens.

Geography is both physical and cultural; hence these chapters present something of the human drama as well as the material base. The former is always more challenging, but too often we have considered only the results of Soviet planning rather than the resources upon which they rest. The face of the earth becomes meaningful only as land and man are interwoven into a single unity.

The Soviet Union is big, diverse, rich, and remote. To evaluate its potentialities, one needs exceptional perspective and objectivity. Side by side exist phenomena that are exasperating and yet thrilling, fantastic but audacious. Despite their shortcomings, the five-year plans changed the country from a land of peasant agriculture to an urban and industrialized nation. It is now clear that the Union of Soviet Socialist Republics is endowed with vast natural wealth. In material terms she has the potentialities for becoming one of the major nations, and the events of the Second World War have demonstrated her abilities to take advantage of them.

The key word in Soviet geography is continentality. Within the Union is room for all of the United States, Alaska, Canada, and Mexico. From Leningrad to Vladivostok is nine and a half days by the Trans-Siberian Express. There are continental extremes in temperature, rainfall, natural vegetation, usability, and accessibility.

Despite the great size of the Union, much of the country is worthless. Too much of the land is too cold, or too dry, or too wet, or too infertile, or too mountainous, or too inaccessible, or too something else. Good agricultural land covers no more than a million square miles, largely within a narrow triangle or wedge bounded in the west by Leningrad and the Black Sea and tapering eastward toward Lake Baikal. Elsewhere there may be the attraction of minerals or timber or local oases, but climatic barriers have restricted normal settlement over vast areas. Within this fertile triangle are most of the farms, cities, railroads, industries, and things

The summer theater in Astrakhan is representative of the older style of wooden architecture. (*Sovfoto*)

Modernistic architecture is found in all parts of the U.S.S.R., as in this government house in Minsk. (*Sovfoto*)

Many spoken languages have been reduced to writing under the Soviets. These are Buriat-Mongols listening to their native newspaper being read. *(Sovfoto)*

All Russians love to sing. Here are the members of a collective-farm chorus near Stalingrad. *(Sovfoto)*

which make the Union strong. This triangle is the essential part of the U.S.S.R.

Although landlocked continentality is obvious, the Soviet Union at the same time has the longest coast line of any country, and the most useless. Frozen seas bar access for most of the year. Even the rivers flow in the wrong direction. The Volga ends in the isolated Caspian, and the Ob, Yenisei, and Lena point to the Arctic Ocean. Even the Amur bends north before joining the Pacific. The Don and the Dnieper enter the Black Sea, but it too is enclosed. Nowhere does the country border an open ice-free ocean except at Murmansk in the extreme northwest. How different might have been the country's history and economics if her continental position had been modified by easy access to the ocean!

Russian geographers have long lamented this frozen sea. The czarist regime made feeble efforts to navigate the Arctic, but the Soviets are actively developing the Northern Sea Route. Scores of steamers call at Siberian ports during the brief summer period of open water, and a few dozen make the complete transit from Murmansk to Vladivostok, aided by icebreakers and scouting planes. If Arctic navigation proves dependable in linking the Atlantic and Pacific coasts of the Union, it may compare in significance with the Panama Canal for the United States.

Like the United States, the U.S.S.R. faces two ways and has interests in both Europe and Asia. America's neighbors are across the seas, while those of the Soviet Union, on all frontiers except the west, lie across deserts and mountains. The country is influenced by its position in an isolated part of Asia and the climatically least desirable portion of Europe, remote from the Atlantic. This position would be a disadvantage were not the Union's economy largely self-sufficient because of the abundant resources within the country.

Global location with respect to other countries is of less importance in a self-sufficient socialist economy than with capitalist interdependence. When one crosses the borders of the Soviet Union, it is like entering another world. The country's continental position is obvious, but the U.S.S.R. might as well be in the South Pacific so far as significant international trade or cultural interchange is concerned. Military strategy changes this isolation, but during the interwar decades, external relations were surprisingly incidental. Perhaps this is another reflection of continentality and self-sufficiency. It may be questioned whether this country, under whatever form of government, will ever play an aggressive role on the international stage. That it will be important, however, is inescapable.

The factors which give the Soviet Union its geographic coherence are its great expanse of level land; its isolation by oceans, deserts, and mountains; the pioneering achievements in agriculture and industry which are transforming the landscape; and its unique political structure. These all make it a phenomenon as well as a place. This unity is offset by the diversity of nationalities, by the wide contrasts in climate and usability, and by the difficulty of communications. Such problems are implicit in the fact that this is the most continental of all countries, compact yet diffuse. No one could expect that Russia would have duplicated the history of a maritime power such as Britain.

It is well to remember that the geography of much of the U.S.S.R. is more easily comparable with that of Canada than with that of the United States. Climatic conditions place severe limitations on agricultural possibilities in each continent. Almost all of the Soviet Union lies north of the United States, for the Black and Caspian seas are in the latitude of the Great Lakes. Fortunately no Rocky Mountains keep out moderating Atlantic influences. Where the Union extends farthest south in Middle Asia, conditions resemble Nebraska and Utah. The exceptions are the cotton and fig country of the southern oases, the citrus and tea east of the Black Sea, and the rice of the Pacific Maritime Province.

HISTORY

The beginnings of Russia as a political unit go back to a series of independent Slavic principalities in the ninth century, united by adventuresome Varangian princes from Sweden. Conflicts between these principalities were interrupted by the Mongol invasions from 1238 to 1462, when the Golden Horde established its capital on the lower Volga.

With the Czardom of Muscovy under Ivan III (1462-1505) came a succession of autocratic rulers who enlarged the territory to its present limits. Notable among them was Ivan the Terrible (1533-1584), who pushed back the Tatars through Cossack colonists, and pressed westward into Lithuania and Poland. Under subsequent rulers, the Ukraine, or Little Russia, was frequently a battleground with Poland. In 1580 the Cossack bandit Yermak crossed the Urals and captured the town of Sibir on the Irtysh. This started the conquest of Siberia which brought Russia to the Pacific in 1639. Following Bering's discovery of Alaska in 1741, colonists pushed south to within 40 miles of San Francisco in 1812, and Russia retained a foothold in North America until the sale of Alaska in 1867.

Peter the Great (1689-1725) was the unifier of the country. So great was his contribution to the expansion and westernization of Russia that the Soviets have now accepted him as the first revolutionary leader. As happened so often in Russia, this strong ruler was followed by a period of weakness and war, which continued until the progressive and expansionist reign of the German princess Catherine II (1762-1796). Under Alexander I (1801-1825) occurred Napoleon's march on Moscow in 1812. Alexander II (1855-1881) instituted extensive reforms, in contrast to the repressive measures of previous czars, but the economic condition of the peasantry was only slightly improved and revolutionary propaganda grew through secret societies until he was assassinated by terrorists. Then followed a frankly reactionary period under Alexander III (1881-1894) and Nicholas II (1894-1917). Southward expansion was marked by the conquest of Bessarabia in 1812, the Caucasus in 1864, and Turkestan in 1881.

Russia did not share in the intellectual stimulus of the Renaissance, nor was she influenced by the Reformation. French culture, however, was very influential, particularly under the reign of Catherine.

Revolutionary movements in Russia are of long standing. In 1825 came the Decembrist outbreak, inspired in part by Russians who had been in France during the French Revolution. The revolution of 1905 was premature but resulted in the formation of a parliamentary Duma. Following the reverses of the First World War, victory went to the Bolshevik party. After a series of revolutionary governments, the Russian Soviet Socialist Republic was established on Nov. 7, 1917, under Lenin, followed in 1923 by the Union of Soviet Socialist Republics.

Since the days of Peter the Great, Russia has sought to break her landlocked limitations and reach the open sea. Much of the country's subsequent evolution is understandable in terms of the quest of the Russian Bear for warm water. After Peter gave Russia a "window to Europe" on the Baltic, there were successive outward thrusts to the Black Sea under Catherine II, toward the Persian Gulf by Nicholas I (1825-1855), across Siberia to Vladivostok under Alexander II, and on to Port Arthur under Nicholas II. Intrigues in Persia, Afghanistan, Tibet, Mongolia, and China proper are parts of the same story. This expansionist tendency brought Russia into conflict with Britain in the Crimean War, and along the northwestern approaches to India. Completion of the Chinese Eastern Railway to Vladivostok and Port Arthur in Manchuria produced the Russo-Japanese War of 1904-1905.

Free access to the sea is an indispensable requisite for modern nations, so that the quest for an ice-free port was an inevitable part of Russia's foreign policy. This was less true under early Soviet economy; for the natural wealth of the country made possible a considerable degree of socialist self-sufficiency.

In one form or another, this search for ice-free ports is an inescapable element in foreign policy. None of the conceivable routes offer much satisfaction. A path across Finland and Norway is topographically uninviting, the possession of Istanbul would not guarantee access to the Atlantic, the Persian Gulf is far off center, and the reoccupation of Manchuria or Mongolia and North China is hardly feasible. The Russian Bear can scarcely expect to find warm water, even though he may be entitled to it.

Just as Russia has grown externally, so population has shifted internally. For the middle of the nineteenth century, Vernadsky [1] placed the center of population near Kaluga, 36° E.; by 1897 it had shifted southwest to Tambov, 41° E., while today it is near Saratov on the Volga, 46° E. The progressive eastward shift reflects the settlement of Siberia, while the southward component is due to the growth of population in Middle Asia. With the development of Siberia it should

[1] VERNADSKY, GEORGE, The Expansion of Russia, *Transactions of the Connecticut Academy of Science* (1933), XXXI, 391-425.

gradually approach the Urals. The center of area is near Tomsk.

Through the course of Russian history, settlement has pushed into Asia as an advancing wedge. To the north of the occupied land lies the great coniferous forest with acid podsol soils; to the south is the steppe, fertile but precariously dry. Each eastward advance of the wedge of settlement brings a corresponding expansion to the north and to the south.

Population pressure and pioneering lure combine to press cultivation eastward, and at the same time north and south. The northward course of agriculture has already moved the frontier into lands of precariously short growing season, while southward expansion is at the expense of drought. Both movements involve the hazard of famine. The southward thrust is more attractive since there are no forests to be cleared and the soils are exceptionally fertile; in good years, rainfall is adequate but, too often, a limited amount or poor distribution results in widespread starvation.

Siberia has been Russia's pioneer east, just as Anglo-Saxon settlement pressed westward into the New World. The dates are comparable since Tomsk was founded in 1604 and Jamestown in 1607. Siberia was occupied rapidly but thinly, with Yakutsk on the Lena dating from 1632, whereas, in the New World, the settlement penetrated New England but slowly so that Hartford was not founded until 1638. On the other hand, the Trans-Siberian Railway was not completed until thirty years after the Union Pacific.

Russian explorations in the Pacific are more extensive than usually appreciated. They include not only voyages in the vicinity of Alaska but also exploration along the northern coasts of Japan. In early days the supplies for colonists in Russian-occupied America had to be carried across Siberia to Okhotsk. This led to a round-the-world voyage in 1803-1805 via Cape Horn, which brought the discovery of numerous islands in the mid-Pacific. Subsequent trips brought extensive explorations in the central and north Pacific and included Bellingshausen's notable discoveries in the Antarctic.

With the defeat of the Russian navy by Japan in 1905, her influence almost disappeared from the Pacific. Nevertheless, the U.S.S.R. borders the Pacific for 5,000 miles and cannot be ignored in eastern Asiatic affairs. Many of the developments in Siberian railways, industries, agricultural colonization, and city expansion are designed to strengthen the Soviets' hold in the east.

SOCIALIST PIONEERING

When the Soviet Union emerged from the disorder of the First World War and the civil war that followed, her industrial structure was chaotic. Railway equipment was in disrepair, factories had been destroyed, and mines lay in disuse. Consumer goods were seriously inadequate. A severe drought had brought widespread agricultural suffering. Further, the revolutionary shift from czarism and capitalism to soviet socialism introduced profound governmental complications.

In order to rebuild and expand the economic structure, the First Five-year Plan was inaugurated in 1928, followed by two others. In each there was a series of objectives as to industrial and agricultural output, usually involving a doubling of production within the period. In this program of reconstruction, heavy industry came first. New mines must precede the expansion of steel mills, and the construction of new locomotives and railway facilities must precede tractor factories. Military defense took first precedence. Consumer goods largely had to wait, even though desperately lacking. With the Second Five-year Plan, starting in 1933, it was possible to shift some of the emphasis from coal, steel, oil, electricity, and chemicals to clothing and food, but the major attention continued to be on heavy industry. The best years for the consumer during the interwar period were probably 1937-1938. After that, defense took precedence.

It is characteristic of soviet totalitarianism that it visualizes Utopian goals. The leaders propose to create the world's first socialized state, and this end appears so desirable to them that any means are justifiable. Where the development of the state is the goal, individuals must be prepared to suffer. Only time can demonstrate the validity of such a philosophy, but it should be pointed out that the government leaders regard themselves as humanitarians. The spectacular success of the Soviet Union during the Second World War is evidence that the five-year programs did succeed.

When the First Five-year Plan was introduced, the Union was in no position to rebuild through its own efforts. Machinery and engineering aid had to be brought from abroad. Thus steel mills and automobile plants were built under technical aid contracts with American, British, or German companies. Foreign experts supervised the expansion of mines and railroads. To finance these basic essentials, the country's exportable products were limited to lumber, grain, manganese, and gold.

It is now clear that the Union of Soviet Socialist Republics is one of the richest countries in the world. Her coal reserves exceed a trillion and a half tons, second only to the United States. Petroleum reserves are more difficult to estimate, but Soviet geologists credit their country with more oil than any other. Hydroelectric possibilities are great. Iron ore deposits are huge, and within the country are manganese, copper, lead, zinc, gold, platinum, aluminum, and even nickel. Commercial timber covers a million square miles, and there is five times as much rich chernozem soil as in the United

States. Here is one land where a self-sufficient national economy is almost feasible.

Socialism is characterized by planning, and in this geographers play a large role. State planning bureaus function for the U.S.S.R. as a whole and also in the constituent republics. These organizations not only deal with the development of industries and transport but allocate raw materials to factories and manufactured products to retail outlets. Even the probable demand for clothing or nails is mapped out in advance and correlated into the national scheme.

With pressing needs of many types, the procedure has been to select a few for thorough attention and let the others wait until later. Thus the Moscow subway is unquestionably the most beautiful in the world, the Kuznets and Magnitogorsk steel plants employ the most modern techniques, the Northern Sea Route Administration has had unlimited resources, and child welfare is everywhere favored. The Great Soviet World Atlas is without a rival.

It is probable that no nation has ever transformed its economic life so rapidly as has the U.S.S.R. since 1928. The goal is nothing short of overtaking and surpassing all other nations. As a result, millions of people have been moved from farms into factories. Illiterate peasants whose mechanical experience was limited to a plow and a hoe now operate complex machinery. Thousands of miles of new railways have been laid down, thousands of new locomotives built, factory cities of 200,000 people replace tiny villages, and large areas of virgin steppe have been plowed for the first time in history. No scheme is too audacious for Soviet planning, whether it be the development of new steel mills in the wilderness or the agricultural conquest of the Arctic.

If continentality is the basic geographic note, pioneering developments characterize the economic life. No one can travel across the country without being impressed by the material results of the five-year plans. The capacity of the government to achieve is obvious. The pioneering spirit that typifies all parts of the Union is unique. Perhaps no other country in the world has such loyal and enthusiastic citizens. Nowhere else in temperate lands is there so much good undeveloped farm land. Nowhere else is the rural or urban landscape in such transformation.

All this must be viewed in relative terms and properly adjusted for the social factor. In comparison with czarist times, the changes are stupendous. Yet in comparison with western Europe, the country still has a very long way to go. Prior to the Second World War, the Union boasted that within Europe it had become the second producer of steel, occupied third place in coal, and led in oil. This did not mean that there were as many automobiles on the streets, or that the trains were adequate or clean, or that people were dressed as in Berlin or London.

To the outside world, the Soviet Union has variously appeared as a "big bad wolf" about to devour the rest of civilization, a Utopia that may solve all our ills, or an incomprehensible riddle. In reality it is none of these, and yet in some measure all. Climate, soil, and topography impose permanent restrictions in some respects, but in other ways it is evident that the land of the Soviets has become one of the major world powers.

POLITICAL STRUCTURE

The term Russia should be used only historically or in a very loose sense. Russian people live in most of the country, but alongside them are Ukrainians, Georgians, and other national groups, each in its separate republic. Where racial minorities were suppressed under the czar, each culture is now encouraged.

The Union of Soviet Socialist Republics is a federation of republics, some of which also include autonomous republics. The fundamental basis of political regionalization is two-fold: economic and racial. On these bases, sometimes conflicting, the local *okrugs* (districts), *oblasts* (regions), *rayons* (subdistricts), and autonomous areas are grouped into larger *krais* (territories) and republics, and they in turn into union republics. One of the latter is very large and complex, others small and with few subdivisions. Boundaries are fluid so that changes in economic developments may be quickly reflected in the political structure.

Prior to the Second World War, there had come to be 11 union republics as follows:

THE REPUBLICS OF THE SOVIET UNION

Republic	Area, square miles	Population, 1939	Population with 1940 additions
1. Russian Soviet Federated Socialist Republic....................	6,375,000	109,278,614	
2. Ukrainian Soviet Socialist Republic...........................	171,950	30,960,221	38,900,000
3. White Russian (Belorussian) Soviet Socialist Republic..........	48,960	5,567,976	10,300,000
4. Georgian (Gruzian) Soviet Socialist Republic....................	26,875	3,542,289	
5. Azerbaidzhanian Soviet Socialist Republic......................	33,200	3,209,727	
6. Armenian Soviet Socialist Republic...........................	11,580	1,281,599	
7. Kazakh Soviet Socialist Republic.	1,059,700	6,145,937	
8. Turkmenian Soviet Socialist Republic........................	171,250	1,253,985	
9. Uzbek Soviet Socialist Republic..	146,000	6,282,446	
10. Tadzhik Soviet Socialist Republic.	55,545	1,485,091	
11. Kirghiz Soviet Socialist Republic.	75,950	1,459,301	
Total......................	8,176,010	170,467,186	

During 1940, territorial changes on the western frontier resulted in the addition of five new republics:

Republic	Area, square miles	Population, 1940
12. Karelo-Finnish Soviet Socialist Republic........	76,656	469,145
13. Estonian Soviet Socialist Republic..............	18,353	1,126,413
14. Latvian Soviet Socialist Republic..............	25,400	1,950,502
15. Lithuanian Soviet Socialist Republic............	22,959	2,879,070
16. Moldavian Soviet Socialist Republic............	13,124	3,500,000
U.S.S.R. total............................	8,348,094	193,198,000

At the same time, portions of Poland allocated to Russia by the Treaty of Brest-Litovsk on the basis of the ethnographic line proposed by Lord Curzon, but seized by Poland during the troubled years of the civil war, were reoccupied and added to the Ukrainian and White Russian Republics because of the nationalities involved. With minor exceptions, these newly acquired areas had been parts of czarist Russia.

The first of these republics, the Russian Soviet Federated Socialist Republic, is by far the largest and most powerful. Within it are five krais and more than fifty oblasts, autonomous oblasts, national okrugs, and autonomous soviet socialist republics. It occupies three-quarters of the area and dominates the political life of the Union of Soviet Socialist Republics. This is the only part of the Union to which the term Russia might properly be applied today.

Moscow, or more correctly Moskva, is the capital of both the U.S.S.R. and the R.S.F.S.R. and had a population in 1939 of 4,137,018. It is at the center of the old industrial area, and the focus of 11 railway lines. Four hundred miles to the northwest is the port of Leningrad, with a 1939 population of 3,191,304. Within the European portion of the Russian Soviet Federated Socialist Republic are a score of roughly equal-sized oblasts, each dominated by a city such as Moscow, Gorki, formerly Nizhni-Novgorod (644,116 in 1939), Rostov-on-Don (510,253 in 1939), or Stalingrad (445,-476 in 1939). There are also a dozen autonomous soviet socialist republics set up because of their non-Russian population, including the Bashkir, Daghestan, and Tatar A.S.S.R. East of the Urals the political units are larger and more complicated. They include oblasts with capital cities such as Sverdlovsk (425,544 in 1939) and Novosibirsk (405,589 in 1939); large krais such as the Krasnoyarsk and Far Eastern Krai, and the huge Yakut Autonomous Soviet Socialist Republic.

The Ukrainian Soviet Socialist Republic includes two large cities, the capital at Kiev (846,293 in 1939), and industrial Kharkov (833,432 in 1939). There are a score of oblasts, reaching into former Polish territory around Lwow (pronounced lvo͞of). Within the republic are the great coal and iron areas of Donets and Krivoi Rog.

The White Russian S.S.R. occupies an area west of Moscow, extending into former eastern Poland. The capital is Minsk (238,772 in 1939). The name apparently results from the characteristic white clothing formerly worn by the peasants. To avoid confusion between the political implications of whites and reds, it is better to use the Russian name of Belorussia. In national terms, the eastern Slavs have long been divided into the Great Russians, characteristically living in the R.S.F.S.R., the White Russians, and the Little Russians in the Ukraine.

The Caucasus is a region of diverse nationalities. What was once the Transcaucasian S.S.R. is now divided into three union republics, the Georgian or Gruzian S.S.R. with its capital at Tbilisi, formerly Tiflis (519,175 in 1939), the Azerbaidzhanian S.S.R. with its capital at Baku (809,347 in 1939), and the Armenian S.S.R. with the capital at Erevan (200,031 in 1939).

The large area east of the Caspian and south of Siberia was once known as Turkestan, but the name is no longer applicable since the Turkmenian S.S.R. occupies only a small part of the desert. Its capital is Ashkhabad (126,580 in 1939). East of it is the Uzbek S.S.R. centered at Tashkent (585,005 in 1939); farther on is the Tadzhik S.S.R. whose capital is Stalinabad. The short-grass area next to Siberia was once known as the Kirghiz Steppe, but the name is not now correct since the Kirghiz S.S.R. is located in the southeastern corner of Soviet Middle Asia, with its capital at Frunze. Covering the former Kirghiz Steppe is the huge Kazakh S.S.R., whose center is Alma-Ata (230,528 in 1939).

Under the constitution of 1936, the highest governing body is the Supreme Soviet. One chamber is called the Soviet of the Union, with one deputy elected directly from each 300,000 citizens, and the other is the Soviet of Nationalities, also elected directly but apportioned among the various republics and national areas. Each local area has considerable autonomy in its internal affairs.

Adjoining the Union are two satellite countries which, while independent, nevertheless have close economic ties with the Union. They have not yet achieved full socialism but are under the tutelage of the U.S.S.R. These are the Mongolian People's Republic and Tannu Tuva or the Tuvinian People's Republic. Both are acknowledged to be under Chinese suzerainty, but there has been no effective Chinese influence for decades.

SOVIET CITY POPULATION

Census of Jan. 17, 1939

All cities over 100,000, and selected cities below that figure

Moscow	4,137,018	Nizhni Tagil	159,864
Leningrad	3,191,304	Penza	157,145
Kiev	846,293	Smolensk	156,677
Kharkov	833,432	Shakhty	155,081
Baku	809,347	Barnaul	148,129
Gorki	644,116	Dnieprodzerzinsk	147,829
Odessa	604,223	Magnitogorsk	145,870
Tashkent	585,005	Gomel	144,169
Tbilisi	519,175	Kirov	143,181
Rostov-on-Don	510,253	Simferopol	142,678
Dniepropetrovsk	500,662	Tomsk	141,215
Stalino	462,395	Ribinsk	139,011
Stalingrad	445,476	Samarkand	134,346
Sverdlovsk	425,544	Kemerovo	132,978
Novosibirsk	405,589	Poltava	130,305
Kazan	401,665	Ulan-Ude	129,417
Kuibyshev	390,267	Ordzhonikidze (North Osse-	
Saratov	375,860	tian A.S.S.R.)	127,172
Voronezh	326,836	Ashkhabad	126,580
Yaroslavl	298,065	Tambov	121,285
Zaporozhe	289,188	Kostroma	121,205
Ivanovo	285,069	Kursk	119,972
Arkhangelsk	281,091	Murmansk	117,054
Omsk	280,716	Sevastopol	111,946
Chelyabinsk	273,127	Orel	110,567
Tula	272,403	Semipalatinsk	109,779
Molotov (Perm)	255,196	Gorlovka	108,693
Astrakhan	253,655	Prokopyevsk	107,227
Ufa	245,863	Kerch	104,471
Irkutsk	243,380	Dzerzinsk	103,415
Makeyevka	240,145	Chita	102,555
Minsk	238,772	Ulyanovsk	102,106
Alma-Ata	230,528	Kirovograd (Ukrainian	
Mariupol	222,427	S.S.R.)	100,331
Kalinin	216,131	Zlatoust	99,272
Voroshilovgrad	213,007	Novorossisk	95,280
Vladivostok	206,432	Vologda	95,194
Krasnodar	203,946	Frunze	92,659
Erivan	200,031	Petropavlovsk	91,678
Khabarovsk	199,364	Makhach-Kala	86,847
Krivoi Rog	197,621	Kokand	84,665
Krasnoyarsk	189,999	Stalinabad	82,540
Taganrog	188,808	Batumi	70,807
Izhevsk	175,740	Komsomolsk	70,746
Chkalov	172,925	Maikop	67,302
Grozny	172,468	Cheremkhovo	65,907
Stalinsk	169,538	Blagoveschensk	58,761
Vitebsk	167,424	Nikopol	57,841
Nikolayev	167,108	Bukhara	50,382
Karaganda	165,937		

2

THE PATTERN OF EURASIA

WITHIN Eurasia lies two-fifths of the earth's area and here live four-fifths of all mankind. The Soviet Union spreads across the northern third of this supercontinent, and many of its characteristics are derived from its position within this great land mass. Soviet geography cannot be understood apart from the continent as a whole. High mountains, broad deserts, and peninsulas divide Eurasia into contrasting environments. The separate nations have hitherto had but limited overland contacts and have developed diverse cultures. Communications have been outward by sea, rather than inward by land. Hence the peoples of Eurasia have but little continental consciousness. In place of the external and centrifugal interests of the past, will the air age develop centripetal unity within the continent tomorrow?

The significance of Eurasia and its peoples does not arise merely from its great size, or the remoteness of its interior from maritime influences, or its climatic extremes, or its diversity. No other continent is so human, the product of so ancient a civilization. The peoples of Eurasia deserve attention because of their unique characteristics. The Chinese have a mature and practical civilization; the people of India are philosophical; the Russians have created a new and dynamic society; and the British have developed a world-wide mercantile commonwealth.

If it were possible to fly high enough to see all of the continent at one time, the people and the cultivated fields

Rafts of timber are common sights on all the rivers in the north. This is a view of the Kama in the Sverdlovsk area. (*Sovfoto*)

Flax is widely grown for both fiber and seed, especially in the cooler and wetter areas. These plants are four feet high. (*Sovfoto*)

Skiing has become a popular winter sport in the Soviet Union. (*Sovfoto*)

Arctic vegetables grow to large size, but their quality is often poor. These radishes are from Igarka. (*Sovfoto*)

would be invisible. One might study the pattern of mountain and desert, but the human half of geography would disappear. On the other hand we cannot know each of Eurasia's billion and a half people and watch how they utilize their immediate bit of earth and, even if we might, we would not understand the interrelated whole. An appreciation of geography requires a combination of airplane reconnaissance and integration, plus the analysis of individual landscapes. Those who wish to understand the regions of the Soviet Union must read both the generalizations of this volume and some of the studies listed under the Suggested Readings. Since so few critical, detailed, field studies are available, many generalizations lack adequate support.

Geography is concerned with all those features which give character and personality to the face of the earth. Since they have areal distribution, they are mappable. For the most part these concern the observable objects of the landscape, but nonmaterial features are of geographic interest as well.

Much of Eurasia is unattractive for human settlement. Despite the pressure of population, only 10 per cent is under cultivation. Large parts of the continent are unattractive to man. Vast areas face the frozen Arctic, millions of square miles are beyond the reach of much oceanic moisture, and this is the most rugged of all lands. Despite these handicaps, it has twice the population density of the rest of the world, with an average of 85 people per square mile, as compared with 40 for the globe as a whole.

The map of land usability presents the features which make so much of Eurasia unattractive. Ruled areas of various categories have either less than 90 days free from frost and are too cold for normal agriculture, or have too little rain (Koeppen *BS* symbol), or are too steep and mountainous for cultivation. Hilly land is stippled and, if not otherwise eliminated, is generally available for limited crop pro-

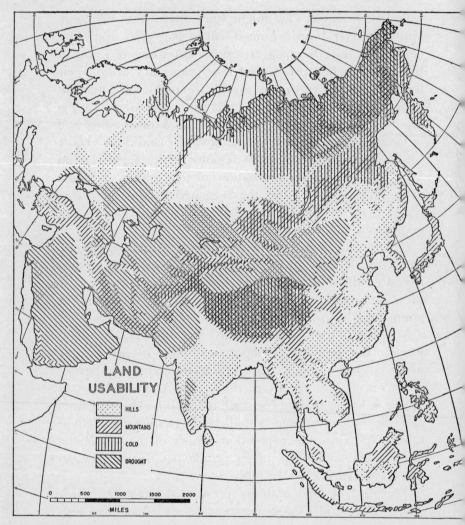

LAND USABILITY

- ⋮ HILLS
- ╱ MOUNTAINS
- ‖ COLD
- ╲ DROUGHT

0   500   1000   1500   2000
MILES

Vast sections of Eurasia are too hilly or too mountainous, too cold or too hot, too dry or too wet, or otherwise too unattractive to provide a home for many people. Only the unshaded areas are adapted to widespread agricultural use, and the northern portion of these lands in the Soviet Union has precariously short frost-free periods.

ACCESSIBILITY

IN TERMS OF 20 MILE STRIPS ALONG

RAILWAYS
MOTOR ROADS
NAVIGABLE RIVERS

0   500   1000   1500   2000

MILES

Large areas in Soviet Siberia and Soviet Middle Asia are more than ten miles from railways, navigable rivers, or automobile roads. Transportation facilities are strikingly concentrated in the fertile triangle within Soviet Europe.

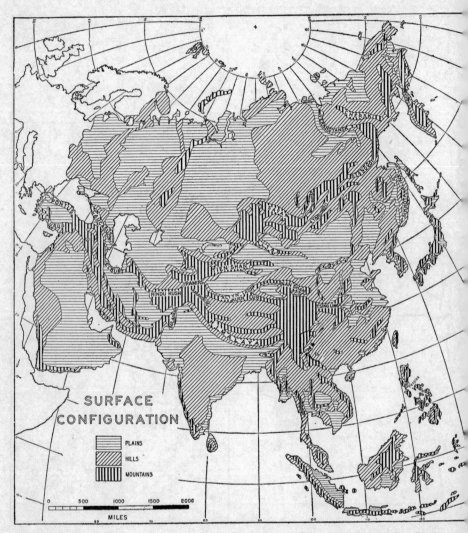

SURFACE
CONFIGURATION

PLAINS
HILLS
MOUNTAINS

0   500   1000   1500   2000
MILES

Great ranges radiate from the Pamirs and isolate the Soviet Union
from its neighbors on the south. This mountain core has kept Eurasia
from having any cultural coherence as a continent. Will aeroplane travel
and new railroads replace centrifugal diversity with centripetal unity?

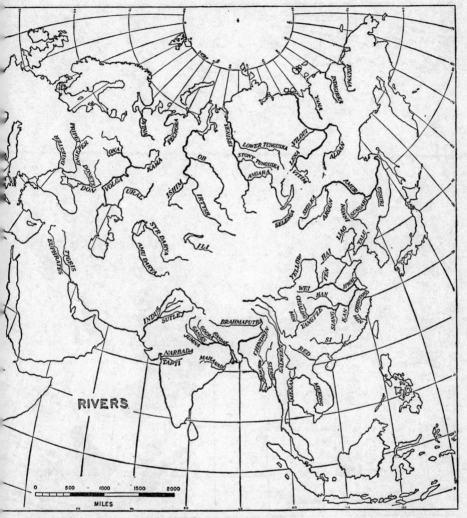

RIVERS

The rivers of the Soviet Union flow either to ice-bound ocean or enter land-locked seas. Five million square miles of interior Eurasia receive so little rainfall that they have no drainage to the ocean.

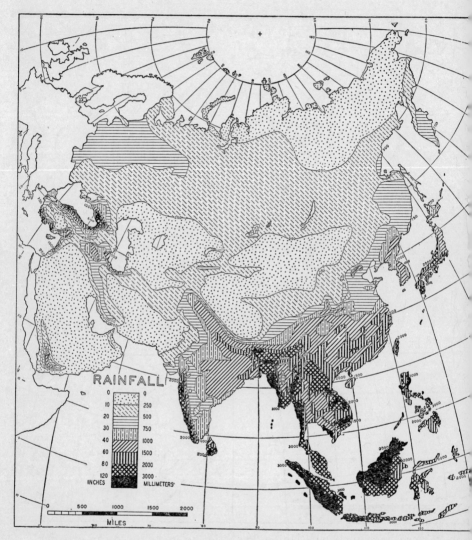

RAINFALL

INCHES	MILLIMETERS
0	0
10	250
20	500
30	750
40	1000
60	1500
80	2000
120	3000

MILES

500   1000   1500   2000

Asia is a dry continent. Soviet rainfall comes largely from Atlantic moisture, as suggested by the tapering wedge of precipitation in the west.

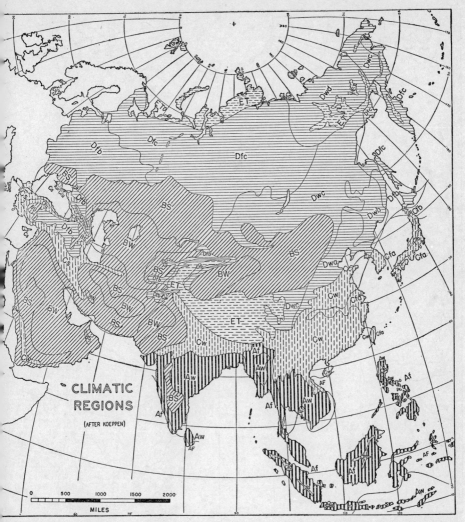

CLIMATIC
REGIONS

(AFTER KOEPPEN)

0   500   1000   1500   2000
MILES

Almost every climatic type occurs in Eurasia, with cold and aridity as dominant features of Soviet climate. This map is based on the Koeppen classification,
in which the following letters represent climatic types. *A* climates have rain and
high temperatures the year around. *B* represents dry climates, modified by *S* for
steppe or *W* for desert (*wüste*). *C* and *D* are temperate climates, *C* with long hot
summers and mild winters and *D* with short summers and severe winters. *E*
stands for polar climates, divided into *ET* for tundra and *EF* for permanent frost
on snow fields.

These major groups are modified as follows: *a*) hot summers, with the warmest month over 72° F., *b*) cool summers, with four months above 50° F., *c*) cool
short summers one to three months above 50° F., *d*) coldest month below −36° F.,
e) no dry season, *s*) dry summer, *w*) dry winter.

106535

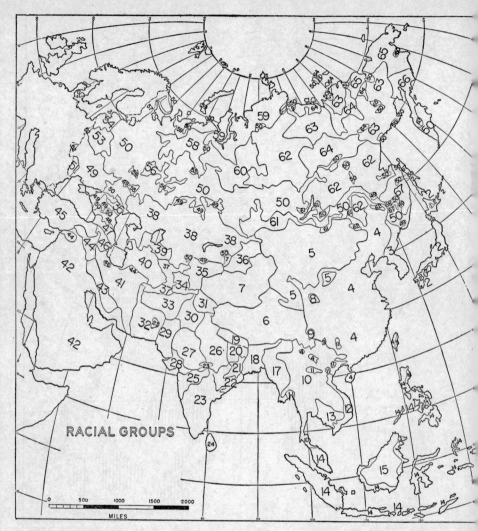

RACIAL GROUPS

Eurasia is the most complex of all continents; no less than 68 nationalities are recognized above. *(Data from "Great Soviet World Atlas")*

1. Ainu; 2. Japanese; 3. Korean; 4. Chinese; 5. Mongol; 6. Tibetan; 7. Tuigur; 8. Dungan; 9. Nosu; 10. Thai; 11. Mon; 12. Anamite; 13. Cambodian; 14. Malayan and Javanese; 15. Dyak; 16. Aeta; 17. Burmese; 18. Bengalese and Assami; 19. Nepalese; 20. Bihar; 21. Mundan; 22. Uriya; 23. Dravidian; 24. Ceylonese; 25. Maratha; 26. Hindustani; 27. Rajput; 28. Gujarat; 29. Sindhi; 30. Punjabi; 31. Kashirian; 32. Beluchi; 33. Afghan; 34. Tazhik; 35. Kirghiz; 36. Kalmuck; 37. Uzbek; 38. Kazakh; 39. Karakalpak; 40. Turkmen; 41. Persian; 42. Arab; 43. Kashkai and Luri; 44. Kurd; 45. Turk; 46. Armenian and Persian-Turk; 47. Georgian, Azerbaijani, and Avar; 48. Other Trans-Caucasians (Ossetian, Abkhasian, Kumiki, etc.); 49. Ukrainian; 50. Great Russian; 51. Moldavian and Magyar; 52. Pole; 53. White Russian; 54. Lithuanian, Latvian and Esthonian; 55. Volga-German; 56. Mordovian, Udmurt (Votyak), Chuvash and Bashkir; 57. Finn, Karelian, and Saami (Lapp); 58. Komi (Ziryan) and Nansi (Vogul); 59. Nenetse (Gold) and Dolgan; 60. Khante (Ostiyak), Kyeti, and Syelkupe; 61. Oriot, Khakasian, and Buriat-Mongol; 62. Evenki; 63. Eveni (Lamut); 64. Yakut; 65. Odul (Yukagir) and Luoravetlan (Chukchi); 66. Nimilan (Koryak); 67. Hebrew; 68. Nonai (Goldi), Ude, and Nivkhi (Gilyak)

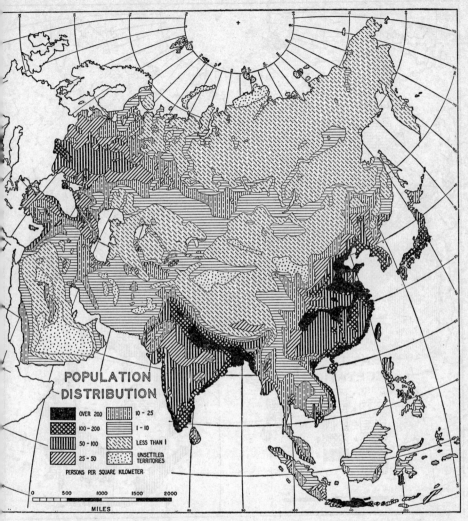

POPULATION
DISTRIBUTION

OVER 200		10 - 25
100 - 200		1 - 10
50 - 100		LESS THAN 1
25 - 50		UNSETTLED TERRITORIES

PERSONS PER SQUARE KILOMETER

0   500   1000   1500   2000

MILES

People live where the land is good, hence this map of population distribution summarizes the environmental potential of the accompanying physical maps. Note the tapering wedge of settlement in the Soviet Union, from Leningrad to the Black Sea and eastward toward Lake Baikal.

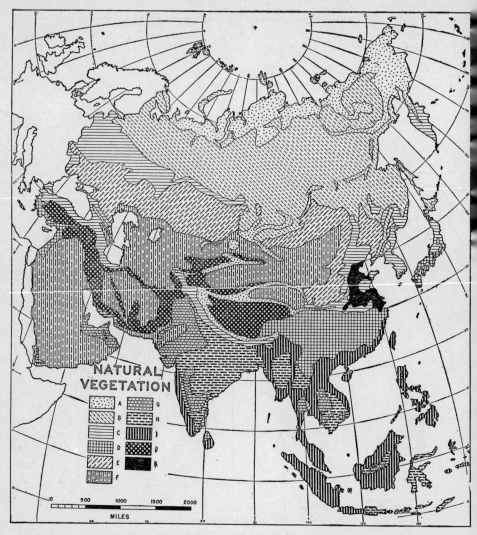

The character of the original cover of vegetation is a guide to land usability. Within Soviet lands, the major types are tundra, coniferous and mixed forests, grassland steppe, and desert. The divisions of the legend are as follows:

A. Tundra and mountain vegetation. B. Temperate coniferous forest. C. Temperate mixed coniferous and deciduous forest. D. Tropical and subtropical mixed evergreen and coniferous forests. E. Prairie, steppe, and semidesert. F. Desert vegetation. G. Savanna and tropical scrub-woodland. H. Tropical deciduous forest. I. Tropical and subtropical rain forest. J. High plateau vegetation. K. Original vegetation unknown.

(Data from "Great Soviet World Atlas," Buck, Champion, and elsewhere)

duction. Only the unshaded lands are really desirable, and parts of these have precariously short or dry summers. Irrigated oases and terraced mountain slopes add small areas. Just because Eurasia is large does not mean that it is all attractive. Too little is really good.

Two unruled and hence agriculturally attractive areas stand out, a triangular section in the Soviet Union which extends eastward to Lake Baikal, and a large crescent in the southeast from India to northern China. The first marks the zone of Atlantic climate and is cool, while the second is the Indo-Pacific monsoon zone, with tropical influences. Much of eastern Siberia is both cold and mountainous. Large parts of China and India are hilly and thus of limited usability. Tibet is conspicuously eliminated on the bases of topography, temperature, and drought. Japan and Java are largely mountainous, yet support a large agricultural population.

Eurasia may also be divided into four great climatic realms: the monsoon lands in the south and east, the desert in the center and west including dry highlands, the boreal sections in the north, and the Atlantic peninsulas in the west which make up Europe proper. The monsoon realm with its summer rain and winter drought extends from the valley of the Indus to the central Amur River and southern Kamchatka, and inland to the edge of Tibet and Mongolia. Desert Eurasia reaches almost to the fiftieth parallel near the headwaters of Arctic drainage; to the west it swings around the north of the Caspian Sea. The boreal realm is the largest of the four; its western limits are formed by the wedge of maritime influence that projects eastward from peninsular Europe as far as Moscow and within it are the tundra and taiga with some grassland. Western Eurasia has maritime influences, with cyclonic storms in the north and a Mediterranean climate in the south.

The Pattern of Eurasia

THE DIVISIONS OF EURASIA

Custom has divided Russia into European and Asiatic sections, but this tradition has little geographic validity. Various maps disagree as to the continental limits and do not even consistently follow the crest of the Urals. These mountains are no more of a continental barrier than the Appalachians. No political boundary has followed the Urals for centuries; neither do they mark any conspicuous change in topography, soils, climate, crops, nationalities, history, or economic activities. This conventional line is an arbitrary fiction of early map makers without the sanction of those whose country it divides. Ancient Greek geographers drew their dividing line at the Don River, and properly, since for centuries Asiatic nomads roamed across the plains northwest of the Caspian. In some instances it may be convenient to separate the eastern and western parts of the Union, but any use of the terms Europe or Asia in this connection is apt to be misleading. What we conventionally mean by European culture lies in the peninsular areas of western Eurasia, not in the vast plains of the Volga. The Soviet Union is a single geographic realm; in culture she is knit to Europe, but by nature she stands between two worlds, the Orient and the Occident. The old and largely untrue saying of "Scratch a Russian and find a Tatar" reflects certain Mongoloid relations, but the Russians properly resent any exclusion from European culture to which they are so closely related.

The single mass of Eurasia cannot properly be divided merely into two realms, namely, Europe and Asia. It consists of at least six major realms. These divisions recognize great cultural contrasts as well as physical geography. Several of these subcontinents are more populous and more important economically or historically than any of the southern continents. One of these areas is the Soviet Union, as large as all of North America; another is China and Japan; Southeastern Asia is a third; India, officially known as a subcontinent, is fourth; and the Southwest is fifth. The Atlantic, Baltic, and Mediterranean peninsulas in the west commonly known as Europe form the sixth major area.

This volume deals with the first of these realms. It is impossible to describe Asia without including Siberia and Soviet Middle Asia, and these lands cannot be understood without reference to the balance of the U.S.S.R. But it is not imperative to consider Poland or England in describing the geography of the Soviet lands. The boundaries of Europe proper thus lie along the western Soviet frontier rather than the Urals. The peninsular countries of western Europe have a common culture and history and deserve separate consideration.

These six realms are not merely political or cultural areas; they have distinct physical characteristics as well. Thus the Soviet realm has almost nothing in common with the Indian realm or with the Chinese-Japanese realm or with Southwestern Asia, each of which it borders. When one enters the Soviet Union, he is in a different world.

Prior to 1940, the Soviet Union had an area of 8,176,010 square miles and a population of 170,467,186. The annexation of the Baltic States and eastern Poland added several tens of thousands of square miles and brought the population to 193,198,000.

MOUNTAINS AND RIVERS

Asia is unique among the continents in its mountain core and radiating ranges. Nowhere between the Aegean and the China seas is it possible to travel from southern to northern Asia without crossing mountains. The few passes are a mile or more in height except toward either end. A complex of ranges isolates the various coastal lowlands and breaks up the continent into separate units.

The topography is determined by its geologic structure and history. Within the continent are several major structural units. In the south are the peninsulas of Arabia and India, underlain by an ancient and massive complex of highly folded Pre-Cambrian rocks. These stable positive areas are part of the ancient continent of Gondwana land; they are now locally veneered with young sediments. Northern Eurasia has two other stable areas: one the Fenno-Scandian Shield around the Baltic Sea and the other a similar block north and east of Lake Baikal known as Angara land but better divided into the Anabar and Aldan shields. Other such stable areas exist in China and elsewhere; all are composed of very ancient and metamorphosed rocks.

Along the southern frontier of the Soviet Union, there is a double series of mountain ranges, from Turkey eastward to China, draped as festoon loops, alternately merging to a nucleus and diverging to enclose a high plateau or intermontane basin. The following description is in terms of topographic continuity rather than of structural unity, but for the most part the mountains are geologically young and hence rugged. In Turkey the series includes the Pontus Mountains along the Black Sea and the Taurus Mountains bordering the Mediterranean. Between them is the upland plateau of Anatolia. Eastward these ranges merge into the Armenian nucleus, with almost no plateau between the bordering Karabagh and Kurdistan Mountains. Parallel to this system on the north is the alpine range of the Caucasus which extends westward into Crimea and continues to the east of the Caspian in the low Kopet Dag. Iran is a plateau basin, like Anatolia. To the north are the Elburz, Khoressan, and Hindu Kush Mountains, while on the west and south are the Zagros, Fars, and Makran Mountains.

This twin series again unites to form a knot in the Pamirs. This is the "roof of the world," a highland mostly over 12,000 feet, with mountains, deep canyons, and rolling plateaus. Mountain chains radiate from this center like the arms of an octopus. To the west are the Hindu Kush; southward are the Sulaiman and their extension into the Makran. Northwest of the Pamirs are the Alai Mountains; to the northeast are the Tien Shan. To the east are four major ranges, among the greatest in Asia: The Himalaya, the Karakorum, and the Altyn Tagh—Kuen Lun. These surround the great highland of Tibet with its plains and lesser ranges. In eastern Tibet there is a third knot or nucleus, formed where the Kuen Lun and The Himalaya approach each other.

Northeastern Asia has an independent sequence. The Altai is a narrow range that projects into Mongolia from Siberia, where it joins the Sayan Mountains on the east. The Yablonovi Mountains extend northeast from Lake Baikal and merge with the Stanovoi Mountains, incorrectly located on many maps. In the extreme northeast are the Verkhoyansk, Cherski, and Kamchatka Mountains.

In addition to these mountain systems, several other topographic units need to be added. The plateaus of Anatolia, Iran, and Tibet have already been listed. Other plateau or related areas are Arabia, the Deccan of peninsular India, Mongolia, and the Central Siberian Platform.

In the middle of Asia are three lowlands: the Tarim and Dzungarian basins of western China and the Turan Basin in Soviet Middle Asia, east of the Caspian Sea.

No single river predominates, as in North or South America; instead a series of great rivers radiate from the interior. Five million square miles are without drainage to the ocean.

Scant rainfall and excessive evaporation do not supply enough water to fill the interior basins to overflowing. During an earlier period of greater humidity, the Aral Sea expanded and overflowed to the enlarged Caspian, which in turn drained into the Black Sea.

Along the Arctic Coast are three great rivers: the Ob, Yenisei, and Lena, each among the 11 longest in the world; and five smaller rivers: the Dvina, Pechora, Yana, Indigirka, and Kolyma. Pacific drainage accounts for four major rivers, again among the 11 longest: the Amur, Hwang or Yellow, Yangtze, and Mekong. The Indian Ocean receives three rivers large in volume but of lesser length: the Brahmaputra, Ganges, and Indus. The Black Sea receives the Dniester, Dnieper, and Don rivers. Five important rivers drain into inland seas: the Volga and the Ural to the Caspian, the Amu Darya and Syr Darya to the Aral Sea, and the Ili to Lake Balkhash.

CLIMATE AND VEGETATION

The continentality of Eurasia is best revealed in its climate. The maritime coastal areas present striking contrasts to the land-dominated interior where the seasons are accentuated. The mountain pattern adds to these contrasts. The interior of the continent is nearly 2,000 miles from any ocean. Other continents extend north and south and are more exposed to the "prevailing westerlies" or to the easterly trade winds. Eurasia stretches east and west for more than halfway around the earth. It has the lowest recorded temperatures for any inhabited place, and some of the highest. Rainfall also shows very great extremes. Winters in the interior are much colder than at corresponding latitudes in North America.

Almost every known climate occurs, from the equatorial

rainy type of Malaya to the ice field climate of Nova Zemlya. Each of the principal Koeppen symbols is included.

The simplest explanation of these climatic characteristics concerns the mid-latitude belt of westerly winds which import moderating Atlantic influences well into the interior. Superimposed on this tendency are seasonal factors that relate to the great size of the continent. In summer the overheated interior warms the overlying air, causes it to expand, rise, and overflow aloft, and thus creates low pressure which draws in air from the surrounding relatively cooler oceans. In winter excessive radiation over the continent chills the air and develops a stationary high pressure area from which winds blow outward to the regions of low pressure over the oceans where there is still a reservoir of warmth from the preceding summer.

These to-and-fro winds are alternately moist in summer and dry in winter and account for the seasonal distribution of rainfall. Where mountains rise in the path of incoming winds, exceptionally heavy precipitation results; in their lee are deserts. This is the seasonal monsoon, best developed in India, less conspicuous in China, and present in the Soviet Far East only as a general tendency. A similar monsoon circulation develops with the other continents but is much more feeble on account of their smaller size.

Unfortunately, this simple explanation is not entirely correct, and the climatic regime of Asia becomes more and more complex as examined in detail. Thus The Himalaya are so high that they block outblowing winds from the Soviet Union, and the Indian winter monsoon is almost entirely a separate phenomenon.

Not enough is known of air mass movements over Asia to present a complete picture, but Polar, Tropical, and Equatorial air may be identified. Polar Arctic air masses move from Nova Zemlya to southern China, and Tropical Pacific air at times penetrates almost to Lake Baikal. Sounding balloons show that the upper air is everywhere moving from the west.

Cyclonic and anticyclonic storms are more important within the U.S.S.R. than previously realized. These moving lows and highs are fewer and smaller than those which cross the Atlantic and enter Europe. Many die out in the interior. They bring with them, however, the bulk of the rainfall that falls in the Soviet Union. As they approach the Pacific, both highs and lows again become more numerous, so that China and Japan have alternations of weather several times a month. In winter weak cyclonic storms cross Palestine, Iran, and northern India, but during most of the year the main path is well to the north; in summer, even near the Arctic Circle.

The influence of the Indian Ocean is limited to the lands south of The Himalaya and east of the Indus Valley. Pacific moisture seldom penetrates beyond eastern Mongolia or occasionally to Lake Baikal. The ice-covered Arctic Ocean contributes but little precipitation, and only along a fringe in the north. Despite the great distance to the Atlantic, this ocean supplies such rain or snow as falls on half of Eurasia. Even 4,000 miles east of the Atlantic, most rain originates as evaporation from that ocean.

Several million square miles are essentially without ocean-derived moisture; any precipitation that falls is derived by evaporation from rivers, swamps, and salt lakes. Since many of these areas appear to be growing drier, more moisture is blown out than comes in. As Lyde says, "This is continentality at its fiercest."

The seasonal extremes of temperature increase from the equator toward the northeastern interior. Near Singapore and Colombo the average of the warmest and coldest months differs by scarcely a degree. Along the Tropic of Cancer the figure rises to 20° F. The Moscow area shows an annual range of 45° F. Peiping and the Aral Sea have a seasonal difference of 60° F. Around Lake Baikal the figure exceeds 75° F. At the Asiatic cold pole in the vicinity of Verkhoyansk, the July average is 119° F. above that for January. Thus average annual temperatures mean little and are not a basis for understanding land use.

No scheme of climatic regions is entirely satisfactory but the most widely used is that of Wladimir Koeppen. Five major types are recognized, all of them present in Eurasia. Tropical rainy climates with no winters form the *A* group. *B* is reserved for dry climates. Temperate climates, usually rainy, with mild winters where the coldest months average between 27 and 65° F. (*e.g.*, −3° C. and 18° C.) are classed as *C;* or *D* if the winters are boreal, with the coldest month below 27° F. and the warmest above 50° F. (10° C.). Polar climates with no warm season are named *E.*

Various modifications are introduced to indicate the season of rainfall or distribution of warmth. Thus *EF,* frost or ice cap, has no month above freezing, whereas *ET,* tundra, has temperatures up to 50° F. in its warmest month. *BS,* steppe, is less dry than *BW, Wüste* or desert, according to the ratios between temperature, rainfall, and season. Various lower-case letters are used to modify *A, C,* and *D* climates: *f, feucht* or moist, indicates rainfall every month or at least enough to tide over a dry period; *w* refers to a dry winter; and *s* to a dry summer; *a* indicates hot summers; *b,* cool summers; *c,* cool short summers with less than three months above 50° F.; and *d* where the coldest month is below −36° F. *B* climates are modified by *k* (*kalt*) where annual temperatures are below 65° F. (18° C.), and *h* (*heiss*) where they exceed 65° F., or they may be preceded by *C* or *D* if desired.

Tropical *A* climates characterize the peninsulas of India and Southeastern Asia, as well as the adjoining islands. This is a monsoon area with every month above 65° F. Near the equator temperatures seldom exceed 90° F.

B climates cover millions of square miles in the interior, with *BS* grassland surrounding large areas of *BW* desert. Summer temperatures are everywhere high, but winters are cold in Mongolia, Sinkiang, and Soviet Middle Asia in contrast to the year-round heat of Arabia, lowland Iran, and the Thar Desert of India.

Temperate *C* climates are present chiefly in China, Japan, northern India, and parts of Southwestern Asia. All these except the last have summer monsoon rain and winter drought, *Cw,* but in southern Japan and the Yangtze Valley the symbol is *Cfa.*

The most characteristic climate of Asia is *D,* present throughout most of the U.S.S.R., except in Soviet Middle Asia and beyond the Arctic, and also in Manchuria and interior Turkey. Where Atlantic influences penetrate the continent in the west and bring year-round rain and mild summers, the symbol is *Dfb.* The northern area is *Dfc,* moist but with short summers. Eastern Siberia has only summer rain and is *Dwc* or *Dwd,* according to temperature.

Polar *E* climates occur in three situations: the ice cap of Nova Zemlya is *EF;* most of the lowland coast is covered with tundra and has an *ET* climate, while higher mountains in both northeastern Siberia and in Tibet are also *ET,* or *EB* where especially arid.

Natural vegetation is the best single summary of the physical environment, for it reflects temperature, rainfall, drainage, elevation, and soil. Parts of Eurasia have been cultivated so long that no trace of the undisturbed cover remains, but in much of the Union samples of original vegetation remain. The general distribution shows many resemblances to the map of climatic regions. The vegetation is described in the following paragraphs by the same letters used in the legend of the accompanying map of natural vegetation.

A belt of tundra, *A,* extends along the entire Arctic coastal plain and inland along higher elevations between the valleys. The subsoil is permanently frozen and plant growth is limited to less than three months. Swamps and lakes are very numerous, many of them associated with Pleistocene glaciation. Mosses, lichens, brush, and dwarf trees form the vegetation. The mountain flora of The Himalaya, Tien Shan, and other high areas is a specialized subtype.

Temperate coniferous forests, *B,* cover millions of square miles where the summers are short and the winters continentally cold. This is the Siberian taiga, a boreal forest of conifers such as larch, fir, and pine with some deciduous whitewoods such as birch and aspen. Commercial timber is limited to the southern portions. The soils are acid podsols.

Splendid forests of mixed conifers and deciduous trees, *C,* occur where milder climate prevails, both in the extreme east and west. Brown forest soils are the prevailing type.

Tropical and subtropical mixed forests, *D,* once covered southern China and Japan and still remain in the mountains. They include broadleaf evergreen trees, pine, fir, oak, and bamboo. Soils are yellow to red.

Prairie, steppe, and semidesert vegetation, *E,* corresponds roughly to the distribution of cool *BS* climate. Dry grasses and low brush reflect the aridity and provide pasturage for nomads. Where the temperature is low and evaporation moderate, excellent grasslands may develop even with 12 inches of rainfall. These regions have exceptionally fertile chernozem soil.

Deserts, *F,* are not necessarily lifeless, but plants are so scattered that bare ground is exposed between them.

Savanna and tropical scrub woodland, *G,* is a result of

seasonal rainfall, high temperatures, and excessive evaporation.

Tropical deciduous forests, *H,* are characteristic of the moist monsoon lands of southern Asia with 40 to 80 inches of rain. Teak is one of the best known trees.

Where the rainfall is heaviest, a dense rain forest results, *I.* This is a lofty evergreen forest, composed of a great variety of hardwoods, often 200 feet high. Mangrove coastal swamps are a special type. Soils are seriously leached and invariably infertile.

The high barren plains of Tibet have their distinctive vegetation, *J.*

THE PEOPLE OF EURASIA

People present the most challenging of all geographic problems. Who are they, where do they live, what do they do, and what of their future? More than a billion and a half live in Eurasia, and some two hundred million are citizens of the Soviet Union.

The anthropological relationships and the cultural history of the continent are not clear. Two maps show the distribution of racial groups and population density. Hundreds of ethnic groups live here, no less than 169 in the Soviet Union alone. In India there are over 200 languages. China is supposed to have a homogeneous culture, but in the single province of Fukien there are 108 dialects.

The conventional grouping into Mongolians in the east and Caucasians in the west lacks validity. Olive-skinned, light-brown, and dark-brown people live in both areas. Head indexes show no differentiation, nor does stature. Cultural history likewise indicates no such separation, for time and again peoples and cultures have moved between the east and the west. Climatic fluctuations in the heart of the continent have repeatedly sent waves of migration into western Europe, the Soviet lands, and China. Griffith Taylor has thus proposed the term Alpine-Mongolian to indicate that the Mongol type is only a variation of the fairly homogeneous group of peoples who occupy the main bulk of Eurasia. These people are all broad-headed. Three major language groups prevail in Eurasia: Aryan in the west, Altaic in the north, and Tibeto-Chinese in the southeast.

The principal features on the map of racial groups are the wedge of Russians in the north, the block of Chinese in the east, and the Indic people in the south. What the map fails to indicate is that almost every group shown may be divided and subdivided. What we need is an unfolding moving picture to show the evolution, migration, and mixture of these peoples during the past hundred thousand years. History is a sequence, of which geography merely shows a momentary scene.

The map of population density equally presents a challenge. Asia has many places where people are few, and a few places where people are very many. No other map in all the book is so important as this one of population distribution, for it clearly shows where people live and in what numbers, and raises the question of why they do not live elsewhere. Subsequent chapters should be read in terms of this map of population distribution.

3

THE SOVIET PEOPLE

POPULATION PROBLEMS

THE key to Soviet strength is in her people. No other Occidental nation has such a reserve of man power, and in no other country have the people been so welded together for patriotic objectives.

Although the Russians are clearly of European origin, two centuries of Mongol domination and the later Siberian expansion brought in an Asiatic element. The plains of Russia were a melting pot akin to those of North America. The genealogical register of the sixteenth century shows that 17 per cent of the noble families were of Tatar and Oriental origin while 25 per cent were of German and west European extraction. To speak of the Russians as Asiatics with a European veneer is surely incorrect. Their alphabet is from the Greeks, but in their mid-continental environment they have acquired a mixed culture. The Russians are at the same time the most eastern of European peoples and the most western of Asiatic.

No less than 169 ethnic groups are recognized within the Union, although only 50 number more than 20,000 representatives. Slavs account for three-quarters of the population, while most of the remainder are Mongoloid, Persian, or Turkic divisions. Where formerly these minorities were subject peoples of the Russians, there is today a peaceful symbiosis. The accompanying table indicates those nationalities which numbered 100,000 or more in the census of 1939. This list does not include the people of western Ukraine, western Belorussia or White Russia, or the Baltic Republics, added in 1940.

THE NATIONALITIES OF THE SOVIET UNION

Nationality	Population	Percentage	Nationality	Population	Percentage
Great Russians....	99,019,929	58	Turkmenians......	811,769	1
Ukrainians or Little			Poles.............	626,905	
Russians........	28,070,404	17	Udmurts..........	605,673	
White Russians....	5,267,431	3	Mariitsi..........	481,262	
Uzbeks...........	4,844,021	3	Komi.............	408,724	
Tatars............	4,300,336	3	Chechentsi........	407,690	
Kazakhs..........	3,098,764	2	Ossetians	354,547	
Hebrews..........	3,020,141	2	Greeks............	285,896	
Azerbaidzhanians...	2,274,805	1	Moldavians........	260,023	
Georgians.........	2,248,566	1	Karelians.........	252,559	
Armenians........	2,151,884	1	Karakalpaks.......	185,775	
Mordvinians.......	1,451,429	1	Koreans..........	180,412	
Germans..........	1,423,534	1	Kabardinians......	164,016	
Chuvash..........	1,367,930	1	Finns.............	143,074	
Tadzhiks..........	1,228,964	1	Estonians.........	142,465	
Kirghiz...........	884,306	1	Kalmuks..........	134,327	
Peoples of Daghes-			Latvians and Lat-		
tan.............	857,371	1	gols.............	126,900	
Bashkir...........	842,925	1	Bolgars..........	113,479	

Only three census enumerations have ever been made. In 1897, the total was found to be 129,200,200, while in 1926 it was 146,989,460. These figures are not comparable as to area, for after the Revolution the country lost 27,000,000 people in Finland, Poland, and along the other frontiers. There was also great loss of life during the First World War and the ensuing years. The 1939 census total was 170,467,-186. Population data for the last two returns are given in the table on page 44, with the distribution between urban and rural inhabitants.

The above total is that of the Soviet census of January, 1939. To bring these figures up to date they should be in-

The Soviet People

Republic	Dec. 17, 1926			Jan. 17, 1939		
	Urban	Rural	Total	Urban	Rural	Total
Russian S.F.S.R.......	16,785,189	76,672,807	93,457,996	36,658,008	72,620,606	109,278,614
Ukrainian S.S.R.......	5,373,553	23,669,381	29,042,934	11,195,620	19,764,601	30,960,221
White Russian S.S.R...	847,830	4,135,410	4,983,240	1,372,522	4,195,454	5,567,976
Azerbaidzhanian S.S.R.	649,557	1,664,187	2,313,744	1,160,723	2,049,004	3,209,727
Georgian S.S.R........	594,221	2,083,012	2,677,233	1,066,560	2,475,729	3,542,289
Armenian S.S.R.......	167,098	714,192	881,290	366,416	915,183	1,281,599
Turkmenian S.S.R.....	136,982	861,172	998,154	416,376	837,609	1,253,985
Uzbek S.S.R..........	1,012,274	3,553,158	4,565,432	1,445,064	4,837,382	6,282,446
Tadzhik S.S.R.......	160,003	926,213	1,032,216	251,882	1,233,209	1,485,091
Kazakh S.S.R.........	519,074	5,554,905	6,073,979	1,706,150	4,439,787	6,145,937
Kirghiz S.S.R........	122,333	879,364	1,001,697	270,587	1,188,714	1,459,301
U.S.S.R............	26,314,114	120,713,801	147,027,915	55,909,908	114,557,278	170,467,186

creased by about 1.4 per cent for each year and reduced by unknown amounts to compensate for war losses. The acquisition of western territories in 1940 added some 23,000,000 people, so that by 1945 the population of the U.S.S.R. undoubtedly exceeded 200,000,000.

No less than 80 languages are spoken, but the main medium of communication is Great Russian. Most of these languages have their own literature, but several had no written records until the Soviets reduced them to writing and introduced schools.

Despite many local peculiarities, the racial problems of the Soviet Union are relatively simple. Slavs occupy the bulk of eastern Europe and have spread across Siberia along railways and rivers. They thus dominate most of the Soviet Union and comprise three-fourths of the total population. Turkic peoples are concentrated in Middle Asia with extensions into the Tatar Republic and Bashkiria in the Volga Valley and in Yakutia. Mongol peoples live around Lake Baikal and along the lower Volga. In the extreme north and northwest are relic races such as the Finns and Nentsi, while the northeast has Paleo-Asiatics and Tungus.

Eighty per cent of the people belong to the so-called white race, but in the absence of racial antagonism there is extensive intermarriage.

From the standpoint of anthropology, the Russian stock is well developed and virile. If the land of Russia has not kept pace culturally with western Europe in modern centuries, it is not due to any inherent or racial shortcoming but rather to geographic and political factors. The position of the Russians as a buffer, midway between western European civilization and the Mongol and Turkic cultures, was both a handicap and an asset. Developments within recent decades make it clear that there is no inherent inferiority.

As a result of the five-year plans, cities have grown enormously. In fact, it is hard to find a center that did not double in the period between the First and Second World Wars. Moscow and Leningrad are the two giant cities, but no others exceed a million. Between the latter figure and half a million came Kiev, Kharkov, Baku, Gorki, Odessa, Tashkent, Tbilisi, Rostov-on-Don, and Dniepropetrovsk. In 1939 the Union had 82 cities in excess of 100,000 population as against 31 in 1926 and 14 in 1897.

This is a nation of young people, most of them born since the Revolution and therefore with no memories of czarism. In 1939, 63 per cent were under 30 years of age and 45 per cent under 19. The preponderance of young people is everywhere noticeable.

The distribution of people is shown in the accompanying population map. As the features of climate, soil, and agriculture are developed in subsequent chapters, the reasons for this concentration will be apparent, for most settlement rests on natural factors. The bulk of the people live in a triangular area bounded in the west by Leningrad and the Black

Sea, and tapering eastward into Siberia. This same area is emphasized in the maps of cultivated land and rainfall. There are scattered extensions east of Lake Baikal to the Pacific and outliers in the fertile valleys of the Caucasus and Soviet Middle Asia.

With the increased emphasis on industry, new centers of concentrated population have arisen in the mining districts of the Urals, the Kuznets Basin, and the Kola Peninsula. Improved irrigation has added to the population in the oases of Central Asia and along the left bank of the Volga. Old industrial areas such as the Donets Basin and the Moscow area have grown. Everywhere urban expansion is conspicuous. Agricultural colonization is especially important in the Soviet Far East.

It is probable that the general pattern of occupance is well defined. The center of population lies west of the Volga, but with the development of Siberia it should gradually approach the Urals.

Settlement patterns conform to types of land use. Where hunting, fishing, and lumbering predominate in the north, people live in compact clearings along rivers, for the watersheds are swampy and overland travel is difficult. In the cleared coniferous forest lands devoted to cereals and flax, villages are apt to be on morainic hills away from the damp valleys. In the fertile black-soil lands of the south, settlements are larger, and typically on high stream banks. Russian villages often extend for a mile or more along a single street. Scattered farmsteads are uncommon.

What will be the future of the Soviet Union? The Russian Slavs, taken collectively, number today some 150 millions, and they are increasing yearly, by the excess of births over deaths, by approximately 1.5 per cent. This rate of increase is greater than that of any other people in Europe except some of the Balkan branches of Slavs. Since the mass of the people belong to the rural and worker population, this increase will probably not be much reduced in the near future. Such a rate of growth of this strong and able stock means a growing biological momentum. This suggests that the Russians must in the future be expected to exercise important world influence, both anthropological and general.

THE PEOPLING OF RUSSIA [1]

Up to the middle of the ice age, the vast stretches of the Soviet Union were devoid of human occupation. Only during the Mousterian or Neanderthal phase of man did sparse human contingents begin to spread over the southern parts of the country. At the end of the last glaciation, or soon thereafter, the early comers had reached the Crimea, other southern parts of European Russia, and as far at least as Uzbekistan, where in 1938 the anthropologist Okladnikov found in a cave, with Mousterian implements, the remains of a Neanderthal child. Farther east, along the upper Yenisei, Angara, and Lena rivers and in the Lake Baikal region, occur the remains of later, upper paleolithic and highly interesting neolithic populations, the latter offering close resemblances to some of the American Indians. Upper paleolithic and especially neolithic men also spread over a large part of the European as well as the more southern Asiatic portions of the country.

About 600 B.C., the region which was to become Russia comprised the area now occupied by Finland, Karelia, Estonia, Livonia, the higher Volga, and the main central regions, peopled sparsely by the Finno-Ugrians, a somewhat Mongoloid stock speaking Finno-Ugrian (Uralo-Altaic) dia-

[1] The author is indebted to the Smithsonian Institution for permission to make extensive use of their bulletin by Dr. Aleš Hrdlička entitled The Peoples of the Soviet Union (1942) in the remainder of this chapter.

lects, and connected with the original Hun, Magyar, Turcic, and other related elements of Asia. At the same time the region that is now southern Russia was occupied by partly nomadic tribes in the east, and partly sedentary and agricultural tribes in the west known to the old Greeks collectively as "Scythians." The more eastern nomadic parts of this loose complex were doubtless Tatar, the sedentary western portions probably early Slavic. Lithuania, then occupying the territory that after the thirteenth century became Eastern Prussia, had an old and probably already mixed European population of its own, while Poland was always essentially Slav.

It was in these earliest historical times also that the Greeks established a number of trading posts and small colonies along the southern coasts of the territory, particularly in the Crimea, the names and remains of which exist in those parts to this day.

In the Arctic regions lived the Mongoloid forefathers of the Lapps, and farther east the Samoyeds.

Over the steppes of Soviet Middle Asia roamed the Tatars, Kirghiz, and related groups; more to the south were the Turkmenian and related central Asiatic aggregations.

In Siberia, the neolithic population had apparently passed into the numerous paleo-Asiatic groups, and well before the beginning of the Christian Era these were being pushed northward by Mongol people from farther south. This large movement of peoples, of which there are many evidences, resulted in many displacements, leading perhaps even to immigrations into the American continent.

The movements of peoples over what are now the European Soviet territories were facilitated by the vast unobstructed grassy flats. These migrations were from all directions except from the Arctic and the northeast but were particularly from the east westward, from the south northward, and eventually from the west eastward.

The "drives" from the east were those by more or less powerful groups of the Mongoloid nomads from the less hospitable regions of interior Asia, where the climate was alternately drier and wetter. The invaders were the descendants of the old nomadic Scythians, now known as the Hun, Magyar, Ugrian, Tatar, and Mongol, and their incursions plagued eastern and even central Europe from the fourth to the thirteenth centuries. They overran parts of what is now the Ukraine, and some reached as far as Poland, eastern Germany, and Hungary. The Huns under Attila penetrated in fact into northern France, where in 451 on the *champs de Chalôns,* near the Marne, they suffered a fatal defeat.

The advances from the south were made by the Greeks, Venetians, Genoese, Khazars, and Turks; those from the northwest by the Goths, Varangians (Swedes), and Germans; and from the west by the Slavs, who eventually spread over wide areas, with later immigrations of varying magnitude of Jews, Germans, Poles, Czechs, and Rumanians. The people of the Soviet Union are thus a mixture of many groups.

The inhabitants of what are now the European parts of the Soviet Union began to be better known as a result of the famous march into their country of Darius, the first "Napoleon," about 512 B.C., and more especially through the writings of Herodotus, about 450 B.C. Of the invaders who were mainly of Asiatic origin, by far the most prominent were the Scythians, whose territory embraced the southern Ukraine. Peoples of related origin covered the country from the Urals to Finland and from the Volga to the Baltic. They were subdivided into numerous tribes and differed somewhat in blood, but all belonged to the Turkish, Tataric, Finno-Ugrian, and Laplandic subdivisions of the great Ural-Altaic stock of Asia. All these peoples, including the Scythians proper, had in common more or less marked Mongoloid features, many were nomadic or seminomadic, none originally being strictly agricultural and, except where they were in prolonged contact with other peoples, their culture was of a primitive order.

The term "Scythians" deserves a few comments. Owing to their warlike qualities and the direct intercourse with them by the earlier Greeks, few "barbaric" nations of the pre-Christian Era have been more discussed. It may safely be said that the early Greeks applied the term Scythians not to a race, but to a conglomerate of peoples, partly nomadic and partly agricultural, who occupied the southern part of Russia when the Greeks began to explore and colonize the coasts of the Black Sea. The main strains of the more eastern nomadic Scythians were undoubtedly Tatar and Turkish. To the west of the Dnieper, however, the principal element of the population was of European extraction, and this stock was largely Slavic.

The Scythians claimed to have occupied for many centuries the country in which they were found by the Greeks. As shown by the remains of their culture uncovered by archeological exploration, they were not wholly barbaric people; and their warlike activities were directed mainly toward Persia and Asia Minor rather than toward Europe.

Scythia itself was subject to invasions, which require some consideration. Shortly after the commencement of the Christian Era, there are noted in Europe, and between Europe and Asia, movements of peoples which are commonly referred to as the "migrations of races," but which in the main were either incursions for conquest and plunder or the results of displacements of tribal groups in regions where the density of population had surpassed the resources and the struggle for existence had become acute.

The first of the historic invasions into Scythia is that of

the Goths. The Goths were of Scandinavian origin, perhaps coming originally from or over the large island in the Baltic which still bears the name Gothland. From this they easily traversed the Baltic and landed somewhere on what is now the Prussian coast, in the vicinity of the Vandals, a related group, who probably lived not far from the mouth of the Vistula River. There they remained for a time; but when the number of their people increased, they moved into Scythia. By the beginning of the third century A.D. the Goths reached the western parts of Ukrainia, the Black Sea, and the Danube, as well as over the Carpathians. They then became known as the western and the eastern Goths, or Visigoths and Ostrogoths; and the latter, with whom alone we are here concerned, were found at the beginning of the fourth century ruling over the territory from the Carpathians to the Sea of Azov.

Goth sovereignty in southwestern Russia was not an occupancy of a waste region by a new race. The territories in question were peopled in all probability by Vendics or Slavs.

The Goths were warlike northerners, who invaded Scythia in some force and brought with them their families. Owing to their original geographical position and their sea activities, they were more advanced in general culture and especially in military art and equipment than the inland populations, who were only slightly affected by the rest of the world. As a consequence, the northmen found no great difficulty in overrunning large areas occupied by the sedentary as well as the nomadic tribes, which had little political unity and no adequate powers of resistance. But the invaders were not strong enough to give the conquered people their language and, though their name remains, the conquerors themselves disappeared. Thus the Goths who gave way before the Huns were merely the usurping and then the ruling class and, when this power was overcome and they were driven westward, they left little behind them that would permanently affect the indigenous populations.

The great Hun invasion which overcame and drove out the Goths and which was one of the most sustained and serious of the Asiatic incursions of all times, obliterated Scythia and disorganized the whole region of the present Ukraine and Bessarabia. The nomadic Scythians apparently receded to Asia; at all events they vanished completely. They left thousands of kurgans or burial mounds over southern Russia, though some such mounds may have been constructed also by other people.

The Hun swarm came from east of the lower Don and Volga. In blood they were of Tatar derivation. Their language, like that of all the native population east of the Slav Russia, belonged to the Ural-Altaic. Contemporary accounts show them to have been typical Mongoloid nomads. From southern Russia they extended their incursions over most of western Europe. Soon after their defeat in France their dread chief Attila died, the power which they had established in Hungary and central Europe rapidly crumbled, their confederates, among whom were some of the Germans and even Ostrogoths, broke away, and what remained of the horde, no longer able to hold its ground, retraced its steps eastward and was lost to sight. Exactly what effect this Hun invasion and occupation had on the population of southern Russia and central Europe is difficult to gauge, but it was probably mainly that of destruction or dispersion.

What remained of the population in southern Russia-to-be after the Hun invasion now became gradually infiltrated with a new ethnic unit, the Khazars, who were of Caucasian extraction and were related to the Georgians and Armenians. There were with them, however, also the so-called "black Khazars," who have not yet been identified. Their history in southeastern Russia extends over a considerable period of time—to the eleventh century. Between 600 and 950 the territory they controlled is said to have spread from the Caspian Sea to the Don and later even into the Crimea. They were relatively civilized people, who built small towns, and engaged extensively in sea trade. In the earlier part of the seventh century they compelled the agricultural Slavs of the Dnieper and even those of the more northern regions to pay tribute. About 740 they accepted Judaism. But during the ninth and tenth centuries they were slowly outnumbered by the Russians, and in the eleventh century they practically disappear from the stage. Remnants of them probably still exist under different name or names in the Caucasus.

The Khazar occupation of the regions which now form southeastern Russia was, however, far from uniform. Waves of Turkish and the Tatar tribes from farther east followed at greater or shorter intervals and over approximately the same open steppes traversed before by the Huns. Whatever the name under which they came, they were all of the Tatar or of Turkish extraction, with some admixtures. All were more or less nomadic and destructive, bent mostly on spoliation, but in the case of the major movements also on penetration toward the richer more central and southern parts of Europe, rather than on the conquest of Russia and the establishment there of a permanent new home. Taken collectively, these invasions resulted in a great retardation of the settlement of the southern parts of Russia. The hordes did not colonize or mix readily except through captives, and they made no great impression on the sedentary population of the region.

Meanwhile, from as early as the times of Herodotus, the Greeks began to hear of tribes such as the Budini, which reached far eastward in the future Russia and may have been Slav, for the root of the term is evidently Slavonic. In the fourth century the Goths conquered the Veneti, or Vends, which was the earlier generic name for the Slavs, the term "Slav" not appearing until after the close of the fifth century. The original home of the Slavic peoples appears to lie northeast of the Carpathians, from where they began to migrate in the first century. The present Bulgars and Serbs represent a southern group, the Poles and Czechs a northwestern division, while the eastern group is divided among the Great Russians, White Russians, and Little Russians or Ukrainians.

During the ninth and tenth centuries many Slav settlements or outposts are mentioned in Russia, mainly by Arab traders, as far north as Estonia, and as far west as the region between the Don and the Volga. Since the sixth and seventh centuries there are also historical data indicating extensive and, in a large measure, uninterrupted Slav population reaching from the Balkans to Pomerania, and from Bohemia and the Elbe over Poland, Galicia, eastern Germany, and western Russia. This population is subdivided into numerous families, tribes, or nations, which formed small units. The term "Slavs" (from *sláva*, glory; *slavit*, to glorify), as applied to these people, probably originated from their frequent usage in personal names of the terminal "slav," as in Jaroslav, glorifying the spring, Mstislav, extolling revenge, Boguslav, praising God, etc. Their earlier history and origin are lost in the mists of uncertainty, and their western contingents, except in language, were not clearly differentiated from the Germanic tribes. Tacitus evidently comprised all of them in his "Germania."

THE EMERGENCE OF THE RUSSIAN STATE

The political unit of Russia did not come into existence until the ninth century. At that time there lived in the regions along the Dnieper and farther northward a group of Slav tribes. These local groups were not yet united. Their dissensions finally led an influential elder to propose that they call some prince of foreign blood, of whom none would be jealous, and under whom, in consequence, it might be possible to merge all the subdivisions into one strong Slav state. The wisdom of this advice was acknowledged and the envoys called on certain princes of the Varangians, of Scandinavian origin. These were three brothers, the oldest of whom was named Rurik. They were offered the privilege of becoming the rulers of the tribes and, upon their acceptance, the Slav territories were divided among them; but the two younger brothers dying, perhaps not by natural means, shortly afterward, the entire nation became united under Rurik. However, in the opinion of some modern Russian historians the real facts were that the Slavic tribes, suffering from repeated incursions of the much better armed and trained Scandinavians, hired other "Variags" for their protection, and these ended by usurping the ruling power over the tribes. Such was the birth of Russia. The term "Rus" appears at about the same time. It is in all probability derived from *rusij,* fair-haired, blond, a general characteristic of the Slav people in these regions.

After Rurik the bulk of Russian history consists of internal accommodations, often violent; of defensive or retaliatory external wars; of endless, fluctuating, life-and-death struggles in the south and southeast with the Asiatic hordes; and of unceasing extension of the prolific Slav element in all directions where resistance was not insurmountable. This expansion took place toward the northeast and northwest, where gradually the primitive Finnic strains were replaced or admixed and largely absorbed.

Notwithstanding the many internal and external vicissitudes of the country, its elementary spread continued until

1226, when all southern Russia fell under the greatest blight that had yet afflicted it—the final and overwhelming Tatar or "Mongol" invasion. This invasion covered all of the present Ukraine, and beyond, and extended over much of Poland, Galicia, and Hungary, with some of eastern Germany. The southern Russians were overwhelmed and subjected to Tatar yoke, or forced to flee. The southern and southwestern parts of Russia became seriously depopulated and were occupied by the roaming Tatars of the "Golden Horde." Russia as a whole suffered from the effects of the invasion for 300 years. The invaders established themselves over the southeastern part of the country, particularly in the Crimea, where they became a fixed element and developed a political unity of their own, which was ruled by their Khans until 1783, the year of their final submission to the Russians. To this day, however, a larger part of the highland population of the Crimea is more or less Tataric; and there is still in the central part of Moscow a section known as "Arbat," which used to harbor the visiting Tatars.

Long before the expulsion of the Tatars, however, the Russians spread over all the northern regions of their present European domain, to and beyond the Urals, and even across Siberia. Expansion into the latter area deserves a few words of comment.

Up to the sixteenth century the vast region now known as Siberia was sparsely peopled by native peoples of paleo-Asiatic, Ural-Altaic, or Mongolian extraction. Most of them were more or less nomadic and in primitive states of culture. There was never any political unity; and many of the groups whose forefathers had probably participated in the westward invasions had gradually lapsed into a weakened condition. It was such a state of affairs that awaited the ever-spreading Russian tide.

The first Russian traders crossed the Urals as early as the eleventh century, and perhaps even before; but such visits led to no consequences of importance. The conquest of Siberia took place in 1580. Yermak, a Don Cossack in disgrace, invaded the vast territory with 1,636 voluntary followers, and this handful of men practically secured the conquest of a territory considerably more than twice as large as the whole of Russia in Europe. Within 80 years after that the Russians had reached the Amur and the Pacific. The rest, until Soviet times, was merely a history of gradual dwindling of the natives and of Russian immigration.

The cultural progress and the racial aspects of southern Russia were affected more by the great Tatar invasion of the thirteenth century than by all the previous ones. The descendants of the Tatars are found to this day along the Volga and its southern tributaries, north of the Sea of Azov, in the Crimea and the Caucasus. The effects of the resulting ethnographic changes are felt even now and were utilized by Germany against the interest of the Union. This relates especially to the Ukraine, or Little Russia. No such subdivision existed before this last Tatar invasion, and the region of Kiev was the old center and heart of all Russia. The Tatar massacres in part depopulated the region and created such terror that large numbers of the people fled westward into Polish territory. There are differences of opinion as to how great the depopulation was, but that it was severe is indisputable.

The language of the new population of the Ukraine developed certain dialect differences. The Ukraine has also received, together with Bessarabia, the mass of the Jewish immigration into Russia. In the course of time there arose in the great territories over which the Russian people were spread some differences in the richness and nature of folk tales, folk poetry, and dress. The Ukrainian aspects of these differences have been assiduously fostered by the Germans as the basis of their cherished ideas of conquest.

At about the same time that the terms Ukraine and "Smaller-Russia" came into vogue, there also began to appear those of Velka-Russia, "Greater-Russia," and Belo-Russia, "White Russia." These names are applied to their respective populations and are partly conventional and partly environmental or geographical. The language and habits of the Belorussians, who occupy the westernmost part of the Soviet Union, were gradually affected by their relations with the Poles and Lithuanians; while those of the Velkorussians or Muscovites, who had spread over the central, northern, and eastern regions, were modified in turn by their associations with the various people of the Finno-Ugrian stock with whom they mingled and whom they freely absorbed.

Such are in brief the origin and nature of the three large subdivisions of the Russian people whom we meet today. The resulting differences between them, cultural, temperamental, and anthropological, are not greater than those between some of the tribes of Germany or the people in different parts of England.

From the anthropological standpoint, the Russians belong overwhelmingly to the great body of Slavs in general. Their cradle is the region extending from present Moldavia to the watershed of the upper Vistula. They doubtless were originally related to both the Alpine European stock and to what eventually became some of the Germanic tribes. But, like all large nationalities, the Russians in various localities show traces of admixture with the Nordic peoples on the one hand and with the Finnish, Turkish, Tatar, Iranian, and other tribes on the other.

An Armenian woman from a collective farm. (*Sovfoto*)

An Uzbek deputy to the Supreme Soviet. (*Sovfoto*)

A Jewish farmer from the Ukraine. (*Sovfoto*)

A typical Russian girl. (*Sovfoto*)

A young pioneer from the
north Caucasus. (*Sovfoto*)

A herdsman from Tadzhi-
kistan. (*Sovfoto*)

An Evenki hunter from the lower Yenisei. (*Northern Sea Route Administration*)

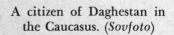

A citizen of Daghestan in the Caucasus. (*Sovfoto*)

OTHER PEOPLE OF SOVIET EUROPE

The Poles are Slavs, derived in prehistoric and early historic times, like the Russians, Czechs, and other peoples, from the common Slav nucleus north and east of the Carpathians. They are mixed with the Russians and to some extent also with the Lithuanian, Nordic, and other elements. Notwithstanding their thousand years of agitated history, they are still a "young" people, full of innate strength, ability, and spirits, and as prolific as the Russians. Their unsettled history has been due to unfavorable boundaries and powerful neighbors, coupled with certain internal conditions.

The Lithuanian territory lay originally along the Baltic, between the Vistula and Dvina. At the time of their maximum political power their influence reached from the Gulf of Riga to Ukrainia. The Lithuanians are now a mixed group of people whose original racial identity is still a matter of controversy. Through their ancient "Baltic" tongue, which has many similarities with the Sanscrit and with the Slav, they are related to the latter. They have an admixture of all the elements surrounding them, the Poles in particular. The Lithuanians, whose ethnographic limits are ill defined, have had long political association, as well as some strife, with Poland; from 1721 to 1918 they have been connected with Russia, since 1940 with the Soviet Union.

The Latvians, or Letts, are a mixed Baltic group related closely to the Lithuanians. From 1795 until near the end of the First World War, they were under Russia; in 1940 they became a part of the Soviet Union.

The true Livonians are almost extinct. Their country lay east and north of the Gulf of Riga, between that of the Letts and Estonia. From the early part of the eleventh century it was a bone of contention between the Russians, Germans, and Swedes, to fall in 1721 definitely to Russia. It is now occupied partly by Letts and partly by Estonians. The language of the Livonians belonged to the Finno-Ugrian family, and they were closely related to the Estonians.

The Estonians were originally a Finno-Ugrian tribe, occupying the larger part of the region of the Old Livonia and present Estonia. Being weaker than their neighbors, from the eleventh century on they came alternately under the influence of the Russians, Danes, Germans, and Swedes, falling in 1710 to the Russians. Estonia remained united with Russia until 1918, when it was severed from that country; in 1940 it united with the Soviet Union.

The Finns represent the westernmost extension of the Finno-Ugrian stock. Although they have retained their language, their blood has become mixed with that of the Swedes, especially in the south. In fact, the inhabitants of the western and southern coasts are much more Swedish in type than Finnish; and there is also some Russian admixture. The more eastern related population, known as the Karelians, is better preserved.

The most Mongol-like natives of Soviet Europe, undoubtedly of Asiatic origin, are the Lapps and Samoyeds. Their numbers are insignificant. They occupy the northernmost limits of the Finnish and Russian territories, the Lapps extending into Scandinavia. The present-day Lapps are much intermixed with the northern whites.

The Finno-Ugrians are located principally on the middle and upper Volga and the Kama and represent the remnants of the primitive native populations that once covered much of central and eastern Russia. They have long been in the gradual process of amalgamation with the Russian population.

There are approximately seven million Turco-Tatars in

Soviet Europe and the Caucasus. They are divided into the Crimean Tatars, Kazan Tatars, the Bashkirs, the Chuvash, and the Kirghiz, with many minor units. They are more or less admixed and have no racial cohesion.

Since ancient times the Caucasus has been the eddy and refuge of remnants of nations, and there are in its fastnesses many interesting units, some of which it is difficult to classify. The strongest single element of the Caucasian population today, however, is the Slav (approximately 40 per cent of the total), which is followed by the Turco-Tatar, Georgian, and Armenian.

Both the Armenians and the Georgians are ancient white units. Both have suffered from many invasions, and both are mixed peoples. The Armenians also occupy the adjacent parts of Turkey and Iran. They are known from at least seven centuries before Christ and are related primarily to the old Tadzhik population of Iran, secondarily to the pre-Turkish peoples of anterior Asia. They are dark-complexioned people, of medium to above-medium stature. They are famed as traders.

The Georgians, or Gruzins, are an old and important trans-Caucasian group, related by language as well as by blood to a number of other tribes. They appear in history in the twelfth century B.C. Their earliest name, curiously, was Iberians, the same as that of the people of pre-Roman Spain, and some connection between the two, though not established, may have been possible. They were among the very earliest of Christians. Their capital, Tbilisi, dates from the middle of the first century A.D. At the beginning of the thirteenth century the country was devastated by Genghis Khan, and this was repeated in the fourteenth century by the followers of Timur. Toward the end of the eighteenth century it was largely under the domination of Iran and Turkey; in the period 1801 to 1829 it gradually joined

Russia, in part voluntarily; and in 1921 it became a Soviet republic. The Georgians, or Gruzins proper, constitute approximately 64.5 per cent of the population of three and a half millions.

The Russian Jews are in the main descendants of refugees forced out of Germany during the persecution of the race in the Middle Ages. Some Jews penetrated into Poland and Lithuania as early as the middle of the eleventh century, but by far the larger number came later, particularly under the Polish king, Kasimir the Great, whose wife was of Jewish extraction. From Poland they spread to Lithuania, the Ukraine, and Bessarabia. Catherine II, particularly, opened to them the door of Russia.

The total number of Jews in European Russia before the First World War approximated 4,000,000, of which 1,300,-000 were in Russian Poland, and 50,000 in the Caucasus. In addition there were about 50,000 in Siberia and Middle Asia.

Under czarist rule the Jewish poor were allowed to reside only in the towns and hamlets of the present Belorussia and of the western part of Ukrainia, in the so-called "pale of settlement." Jewish children were admitted to secondary schools and universities only under a very limited percentage ratio. In 1924 the Jewish poor from the hamlets began to settle on untenanted lands of the Ukraine, the steppe region of the Crimea, and in the northern Caucasus, Georgia, and Uzbekistan. In 1928 the Soviets set aside the Birobidjan district in the Far East as a settlement place for Jewish workers, and this has become the "Jewish Autonomous Region."

The total number of Germans in the lands under Russian dominion at the beginning of the First World War amounted to a little over 1,800,000. They were scattered over all except the poorest parts of the empire, especially in the cities. In the Baltic provinces they were the landed proprietors. In southern Russia and other agriculturally rich regions there were German agricultural colonies, some recent, some of older formation. The main one of these was on the Volga.

The German influx into Russia started in the sixteenth century and was especially active during the reign of Catherine II. They came as artisans and merchants, frequently on invitation; and in 1762 they were invited to settle in parts of southern Russia in agricultural colonies, which gradually and in a scattered way extended to the Crimea, the Don, the Volga, and the Caucasus. These colonies received special privileges, were practically self-governing, and fused but little with the Russians. During the latter half of the nineteenth century German colonization in important parts of Russia was favored and possibly directed by the German government for economic and perhaps strategic reasons.

The German nobles and landed proprietors in the Baltic provinces date in the main from the attempts by the German Knights forcibly to Christianize the natives of the provinces and dominate the region.

After the establishment of the Soviet regime, the Volga Germans, who lived in a compact unit, were made into an Autonomous Volga German Republic. At the end of August, 1941, as the invading Germans were forging eastward, the Volga group having become a point of danger to the state, the republic was abolished, the Germans were evacuated from the Volga region and were resettled in parts of western Siberia and Soviet Middle Asia.

A study of the German relations with Russia shows that the latter has ever been a field for exploitation by Germany. Care was taken that the Germans in Russia should not disappear in the Russian mass and thus weaken Germany to the advantage of her neighbor.

ASIATIC PEOPLES OF THE SOVIET UNION

The bulk of the people in Siberia and Middle Asia today are Great Russian. Among the rest, there are several groups that call for at least a brief special notice.

Of the peoples of predominantly white but non-Russian origin, the principal ones are the Tadzhiks, or Tajiks. This is an old brachycephalic Iranian stock, of slightly above-medium stature, mixed somewhat with the Turkmen and differing physically as well as otherwise from both the Persians proper and from the Afghans. They live largely in a mountainous country which extends on the east into the Pamirs, on the south to Afghanistan. They constitute about three-quarters of the people of the Soviet Tadzhik Republic.

The Turkmen form the principal old Middle Asiatic stock. Where best preserved, they are distinguished by brachycephaly, above-medium stature, and characteristic facial features. They are to be counted with the Asiatic whites, but in various regions there is much admixture with the Tatars.

There is more or less of white admixture in all the remaining Asiatic peoples of the Soviet Union, but the main strains of these are the Mongoloid in the south and the related paleo-Asiatic in the north. Among all the larger groups, especially in Azerbaidzhan, Uzbekistan, and the Tatar republics (Kazakhstan and Kirghizstan), there are individuals whom it would be hard to class as other than whites, but Mongoloid features, in various dilutions to purity, are predominant. In the army, in the physical culture parades, and in the pioneer groups, where all dress alike, the differences are still further subdued and it becomes difficult in cases even for an expert to be sure of what confronts him. It is principally for this reason that there is no "race problem" in the Soviet Union.

Aside from the larger ethnic units in the south, there exist in the vast stretches of Siberia, along the rivers, on the sea coasts, and in the forests, many remnants of ancient tribes and peoples. In general these elements are of paleo-Asiatic or Mongolian derivation, belong to various contingents of the yellow-brown human complex, have more or less Mongoloid features, yellowish to medium-brown skin, straight black hair. Individuals to whole groups among them show close resemblances to native yellow-brown Americans. All these groups are already considerably admixed with Russian whites, and these mixtures are gradually increasing so that within another century or two there will be left only a fusion. Today, however, these groups still exist and have been known by various names, most of which were nicknames or corruptions and have been changed by the Soviet authorities. The principal names, past and present, are the following:

ETHNIC GROUPS

Old	New	Old	New
Abakan Turks	Khakasi	Negidaltsi	Elkenbeie
Aleuts	Unarigani	Orochi	Nani
Altaici	Oiroti	Oroki	Nani
Asiatic Eskimo	Iuits	Ostiaks	Khanty
Chukchi	Luoravetlani	Ostiaks-Samoyeds	Selkupi
Chuvantsi	Eteli	Ostiaks-Yenisei	Keti
Giliaks	Nivkhi	Samoyeds-Iuraks	Nentsi
Golds	Nanai	Samoyeds-Tavgiiski	Nganasani
Iukagirs	Oduli	Samoyeds-Yenisei	Entsi
Kamchadals	Itelmeni	Tungus	Evenki
Karagassi	Tophalari	Udiegeitse	Ude
Koriaks	Uimillani	Ulchi	Nani
Lamuts	Eveni	Voguls	Mansi
Lopars	Saami		

In addition there are in the north the Yakuts, speaking a Turcic language but being decidedly Mongoloid in features;

farther east the Chukchi, now identified as physically the same as the Eskimo, and some of the Eskimo proper; in the southeast small contingents of the Koreans, Japanese, Chinese, and Mongols; in the southwest the Mongolian Kalmuks.

Before the German invasion in 1941, and to a greater extent since that event, the western regions of Soviet Siberia and Soviet Middle Asia have received large accretions of workmen and refugees from Ukrainia and most other western parts of the country, several million in all. Whole establishments with their staffs and workers have been transported there and reestablished. This is particularly true of the Urals, but also of Kazakhstan and Uzbekistan. These displacements have already much altered the population as well as other aspects of these regions. The Urals are rapidly developing into the industrial backbone of the Soviet Union, while the southern wastes and deserts are being developed through extensive irrigation and construction and have already advanced in population and otherwise beyond the old standards of the ancient Middle Asian dominions.

The population of Soviet Asia is therefore in a state of rapid change and great flux. Its heterogeneity is decreasing through intermarriages, and it is receiving a flood of new increments from Soviet Europe. Paralleling the development of the western United States from the seventies onward, there is now going on a transformation of Siberia; a new human world is in formation there—a world of virile pioneers, farmers, and workers, tinged slightly here and there by Mongoloid features, but essentially white, young, and wholesome.

PHYSICAL STANDARDS

Until 1923 the peoples of the Soviet Union presented an interesting biological condition. Hygiene and medical care were insufficient, in places almost wanting. Serious droughts were followed by widespread famines. At the same time the birth rate was very high, reaching in some parts the yearly rate of over 50 per thousand, or more than twice that in other large European countries. These conditions also resulted in a very high death rate, particularly among the weaker elements of the population, both children and adults. Only the stronger and more resistant could survive under such disadvantages, but those who did survive constituted a strong people of a high biological value. It was thus that they were able to survive the First World War, the Revolution, the interventionist and civil wars that followed, and the great famine that developed during these years; and it was thus that they still found strength to drive out all invaders, form a great state with striking developments in many directions, and eventually stand and stem the attack of the greatest and most destructive military machine of all times.

Anthropologically, the peoples of the Soviet Union, in common with all other larger human contingents of modern times, are more or less admixed and present many grades and variants in stature, head form, and all other features. Of the large groups the most homogeneous are the Great Russians. Except where mixed somewhat with the old Finno-Ugrians, they might justifiably be called a subrace of the white human stem. Their characteristics are well marked and include, on the average, light hair; bluish or gray eyes; rounded head; medium-featured face, pleasing and strong but not often handsome; well-proportioned to sturdy body, generally rather short but strong hands and feet. Their stature is not so high, blondness so pronounced, or eyes so often blue as in the Scandinavians, but their lightness is more general than with the Germans. The nose is never over-prominent, the lips are normally never thin, the jaws are strong, the teeth generally regular and in much better condition than in western Europeans or Americans. The beard, where still worn—which is now rare even among the older men—is as a rule more or less grizzly and ample in size.

The Belorussians are in all these respects much like the Great Russians, but there are some differences among the Ukrainians. The latter show less lightness of hair and eyes; there are more plump women among them, and more that are really beautiful in youth. More or less mixture with the Tatars or other non-Russian elements has taken place in the southern districts. In these regions too the people are predominantly of medium stature and brachycephalic.

The peoples of the Baltic republics, from Livonia northward, show occasional traces of the original Mongoloid Finno-Ugrian stock, but all through these parts both Nordic and Slavic features may commonly be encountered.

In Russian Galicia, Moldavia, and Bessarabia, the basic elements of the population are Slavs, kin mainly with the Ukrainians—most of them in fact are Ukrainians, and the type is similar. But there were also here, up to the 1941 invasion, numerous Jews, with some Poles, Bolgars, Rumanians, Gypsies, and other small contingents, which produced physical diversity.

In the Crimea, which contains a mosaic of small ethnic groups with a predominance in the hills of the Tatars and their mixtures, there is no prevalent local type. The Tatars, or what remains of them, show Mongoloid features.

The Caucasus, a mountain complex over 900 miles long and 140 miles broad, with its many native groups of white people, appears to be less of a puzzle physically. There are two main types: that of many of the mountaineers proper and that of the people of Trans-Caucasian Georgia and especially Armenia.

The native Asiatic groups, as already mentioned, show predominantly Mongoloid features.

4

THE PHYSICAL FOUNDATION

THE GEOLOGICAL BASE

THIS chapter presents a critical evaluation of geology, topography, climate, vegetation, and soil. Although these elements of the physical landscape lack the drama of the human scene, they nevertheless supply part of the foundation for Soviet strength.

The geography of the Soviet Union begins with its most ancient geology. This sketch of geology is thus a preface to modern topography and land use. In four corners of the country are old and resistant Pre-Cambrian rocks around which younger mountains have been folded and between which lie great plates of undisturbed Paleozoic sediments. Each buttress or shield is a positive area that has tended to remain above sea level for many periods and so has been deeply eroded. In their geology and topography these resemble the Canadian Shield.

The best known of these shields is in the northwest where much of Scandinavia is occupied by a complex of granite, gneiss, and metamorphic rocks of Archeozoic and Proterozoic age. This is termed the Fenno-Scandian or Baltic Shield, but the only part within the U.S.S.R. is Karelia and the Kola Peninsula.

In the Ukraine are scattered windows into a partly buried area of ancient rocks which extends from the Sea of Azov northwest to the Carpathian foothills. This is the Azov-Podolian Shield. Whereas Karelia and Kola rise 3,000 feet above sea level, the Ukrainian crystalline block lies below 900 feet. Somewhat north of the main Azov-Podolian mass is the smaller Voronezh block. These southwestern outcrops are linked with the Fenno-Scandian Shield through buried connections that follow the western frontiers of the Union.

The eastern corners of the quadrilateral are in central Siberia; one near the Arctic, the other near Lake Baikal. Between the mouth of the Yenisei and that of the Lena is an outcrop of typical Pre-Cambrian schist and gneiss along the Anabar River, from which the shield derives its name. Farther south is a larger and more irregular exposure, partly southwest of Lake Baikal but largely to the east near the Aldan River.

Three of these windows into the Pre-Cambrian are mining regions of significance. The Kola Peninsula has very large deposits of apatite, the Ukrainian area has iron and manganese, and the Aldan Shield is rich in gold.

Four regions of sedimentary rocks lie within these shields. Soviet Europe is largely underlain by a great platform of essentially undisturbed upper Paleozoic formations. Across the folded Urals the West Siberian Lowland is floored with young marine deposits and glacial sands. Beyond the Yenisei are the Central Siberian Uplands, covered by late Paleozoic sediments and considerably more hilly than the platform in Europe. Except for the narrow Urals, there is no major folding in the 3,000 miles from the Baltic to the Lena. East of the Caspian Sea is the fourth lowland, where Quaternary sands mask Tertiary and Mesozoic formations.

Surrounding these lowlands are a continuous series of high, rugged mountains. The outermost of these are the youngest and of Tertiary age, such as those in Crimea, the Caucasus, the Hindu Kush, Kamchatka, and Sakhalin. Mesozoic mountains occupy the area from the Sea of Okhotsk to the Lena. The Urals and the structures of Kazakhstan date from the Permian.

Earthquakes and volcanoes are limited to the marginal

zones. Except for two small quakes in the central Urals, no epicenters have ever been recorded outside the limits of the young mountains. The areas of greatest intensity are the Caucasus, the mountains of Middle Asia, Lake Baikal, and southeastern Kamchatka. Current vulcanism is restricted to the Caucasus and Kamchatka.

The last chapter in geology is often more important than the first. During the Pleistocene, the northwestern quarter of the Union was glaciated, while the eastern third acquired permanently frozen ground.

At least three continental ice sheets invaded the area. The earliest stage was the Mindel, corresponding to the Kansan in North America. The most widespread was the Riis, equivalent to the Illinoian, when a lobe of ice followed the valley of the Dnieper to latitude 48° N., its southernmost limit in Europe, as compared with 37° N. in North America. The uplands south of Moscow blocked this ice and formed a reentrant, but farther east a second lobe occupied the Don Valley, limited on the east by hills along the Volga. Ice crossed the Urals near latitude 60° N., and the boundary continued eastward irregularly to the Yenisei, east of which it swung sharply to the north and reached the Arctic Ocean just east of the Taimyr Peninsula.

Local glaciers spread out from the mountains in the Caucasus, Pamirs, Tien Shan, Altai-Sayan, Baikal, and Verkhoyansk areas, but it is certain that there were no continental ice sheets in eastern Siberia.

The last stage was the Wurm or Wisconsin, but the advance did not reach Moscow, and the Asiatic portion was limited to the Ob estuary and the Taimyr Peninsula. Eurasian ice radiated from three centers, Scandinavia, Nova Zemlya, and the Taimyr Peninsula.

These glacial invasions left a record of morainic deposits, swamps, and deranged drainage, but the effects were not

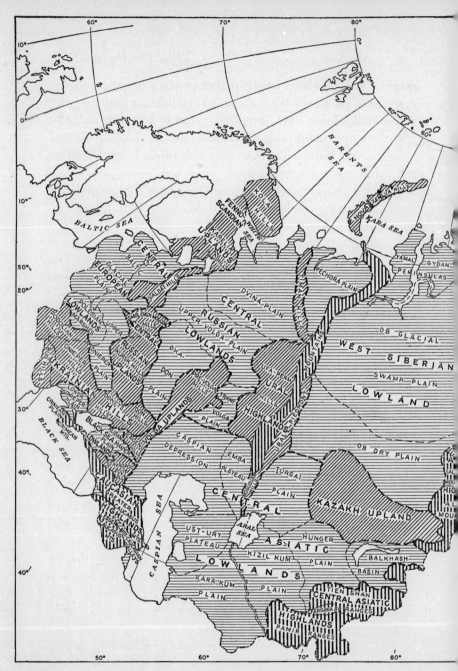

Within the eight million square miles of the Soviet Union are 18 land
and east.

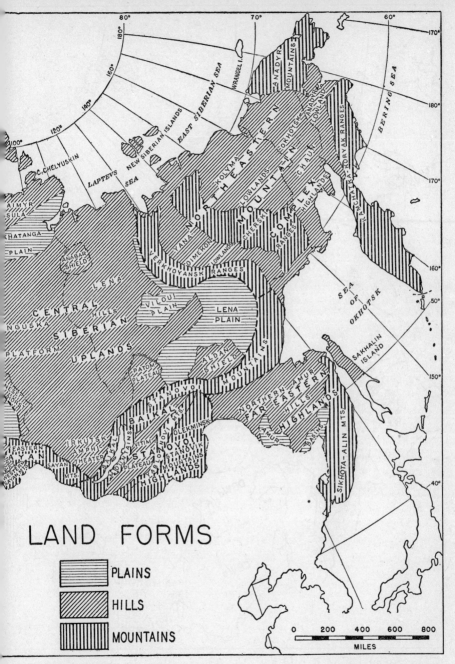

LAND FORMS

PLAINS

HILLS

MOUNTAINS

0   200   400   600   800
MILES

form regions and 82 subregions. Higher mountains are limited to the south

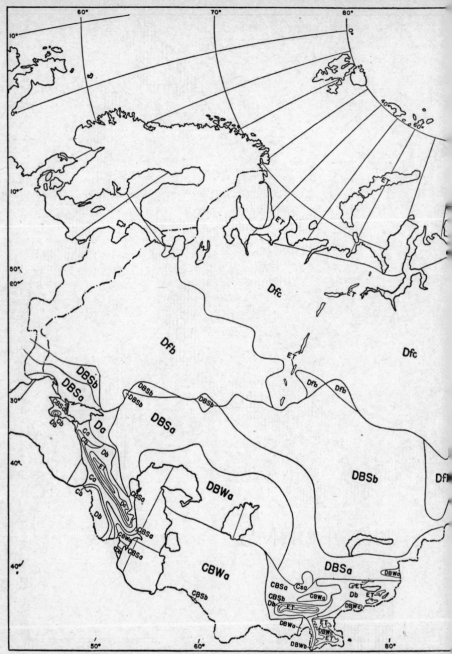

The Soviet Union is cold and dry. These follow the Koeppen system,
Arctic tundra, and *BS* and *BW* refer to aridity, either steppe or desert. Th
over 72° F.; *b*) cool summers, with four months above 50° F.; *c*) cool short
f) no dry season; *s*) dry summer; *w*) dry winter. (*After Voznesenski.*)

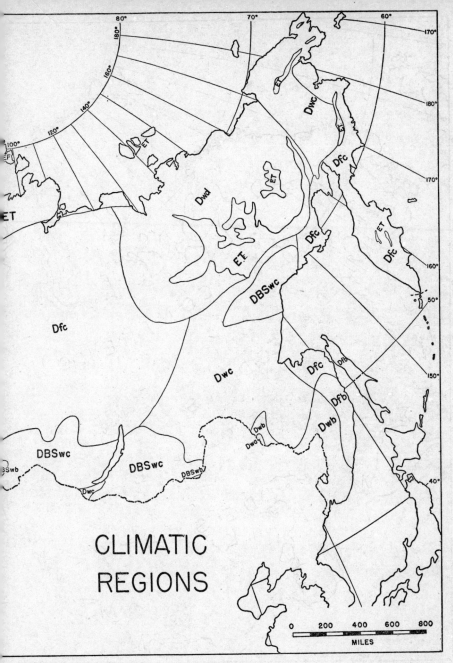

CLIMATIC
REGIONS

0 200 400 600 800

MILES

in which *C* represents warm temperate conditions, *D* cold temperate, *ET*
e small letters are used as follows: *a*) hot summers, with the warmest month
summers one to three months above 50° F.; *d*) coldest month below —36° F.;

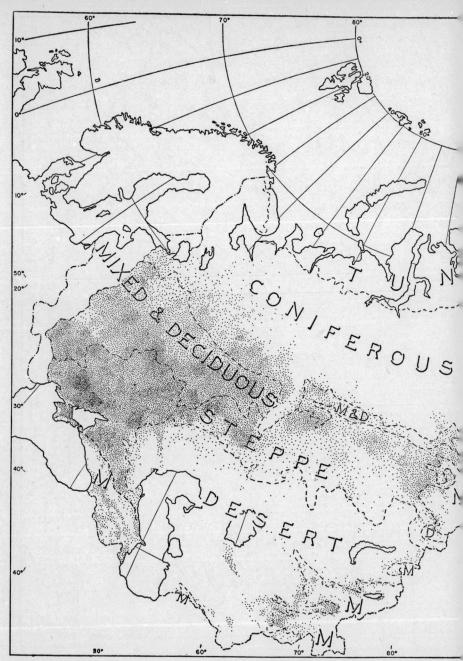

Within Soviet lands are five major types of original vegetation: tundra,
ert. Mountain areas have a varied flora according to altitude. The distribu
ability of the agricultural triangle. (*Data from "Great Soviet World Atlas,"*

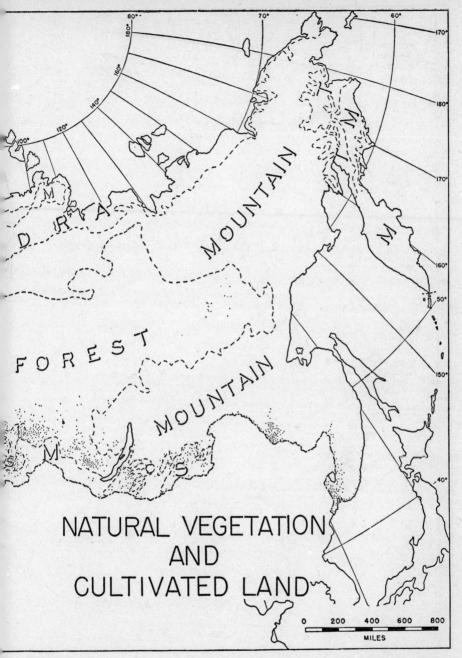

NATURAL VEGETATION
AND
CULTIVATED LAND

0 200 400 600 800
MILES

coniferous forest, mixed coniferous and deciduous forest, steppe, and des-
tion of crop land, as shown by the stippled area, reflects the superior desir-
I, Plates 121-122, 155-156.)

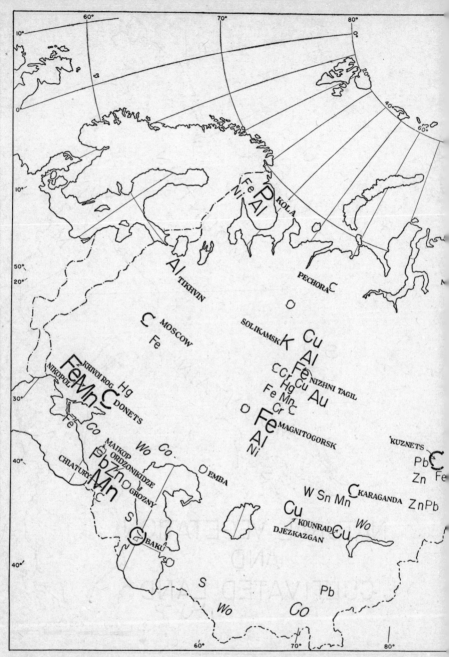

The Soviet Union is the second richest country on earth, with mineral
suggest the relative world rank of the respective resources. Fuels are shown
minum, Au—gold, Cr—chromium, Cu—copper, Hg—mercury, K—potash, M
agricultural products, in italics, include Co—cotton and Wo—wool.

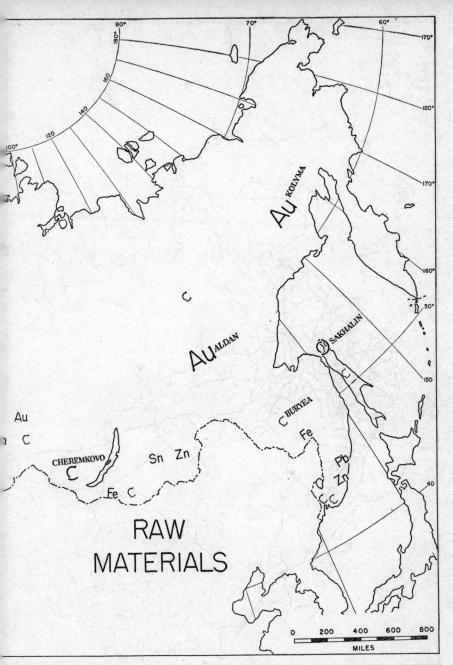

RAW
MATERIALS

resources next to those of the United States. The symbols on the map
in shadow letters: C—coal, O—oil. Minerals are in vertical letters: Al—alu-
n—manganese, Ni—nickel, Pb—lead, S—sulphur, Sn—tin, Zn—zinc. Industrial

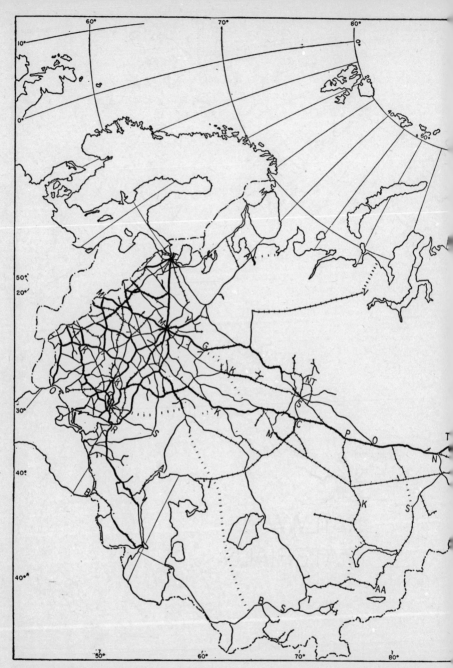

With 62,500 miles of railway in 1940, the U.S.S.R. holds second place in programs. Note the concentration of railways in a triangular area to the

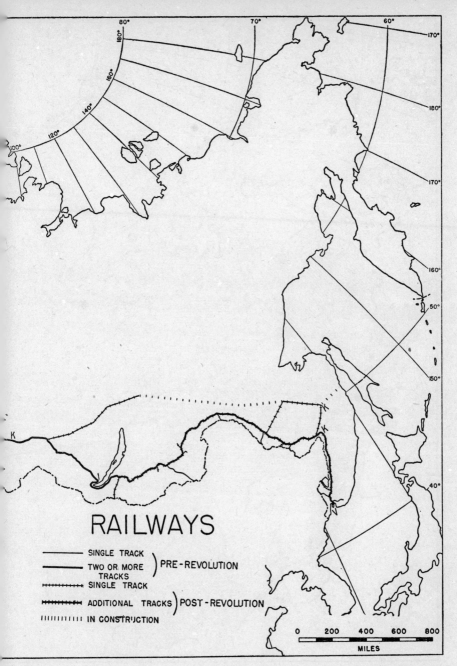

RAILWAYS

————	SINGLE TRACK	} PRE-REVOLUTION
▬▬▬▬	TWO OR MORE TRACKS	
++++++++++	SINGLE TRACK	} POST-REVOLUTION
▬▬▬▬▬▬	ADDITIONAL TRACKS	
IIIIIIIIIIII	IN CONSTRUCTION	

0 200 400 600 800

MILES

mileage. A considerable part of this mileage was added under the five year
west, and the new lines in Siberia and Middle Asia.

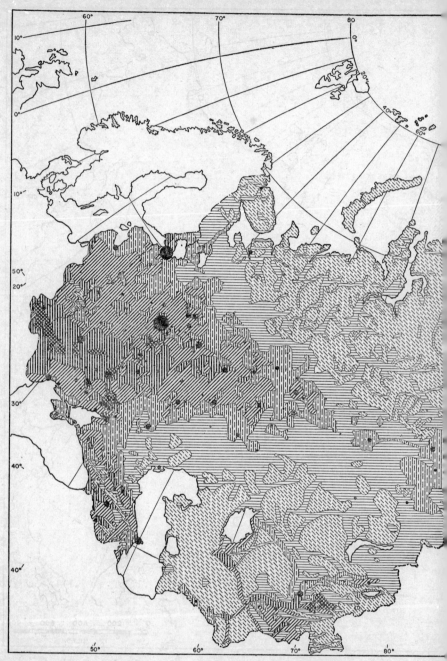

The distribution of population closely reflects the location of agricultural
ingrad southward to the Black Sea and eastward into Siberia. Isolated cen
proportional to their size. *(Data from "Great Soviet World Atlas," II,*

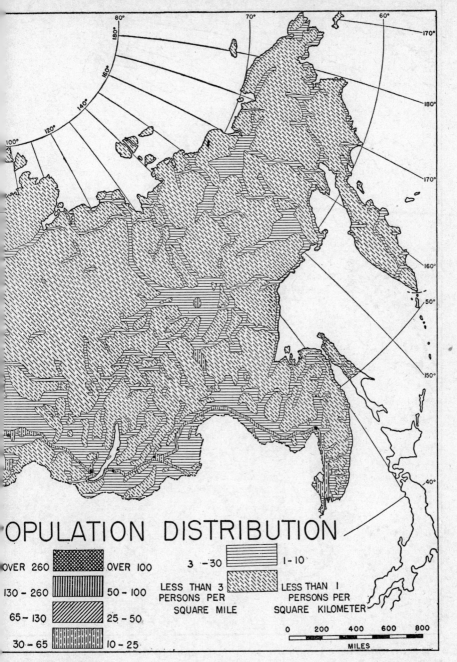

POPULATION DISTRIBUTION

OVER 260	OVER 100	3 – 30	1 – 10
130 – 260	50 – 100	LESS THAN 3 PERSONS PER SQUARE MILE	LESS THAN 1 PERSONS PER SQUARE KILOMETER
65 – 130	25 – 50		
30 – 65	10 – 25		

0   200   400   600   800
MILES

land. Most people of the Soviet Union live in a triangular area from Len-
ters in Middle Asia reflect local irrigation. Cities are shown by black dots
Plates 11, 12.)

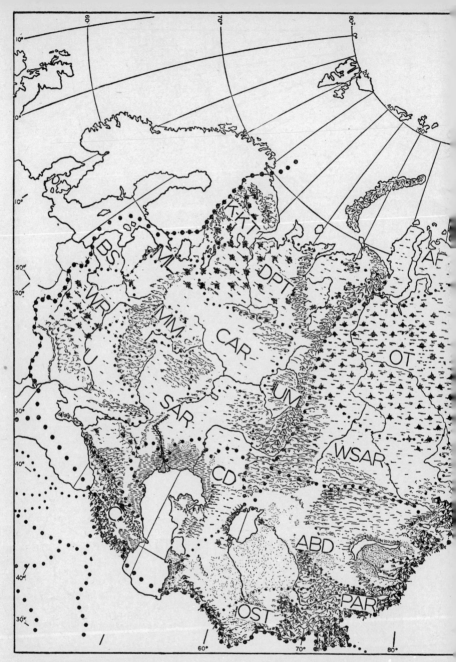

Within the Soviet Union are three geographic provinces and 24 regions. Metropolitan Leningrad, the Kola-Karelia Taiga, the Dvina-Pechora Taiga, cultural Region, and the Ural Mountains. Soviet Middle Asia includes C Southern Turan, and the Aral-Balkhash Deserts. Soviet Siberia is composed Ob Taiga, the Yenisei Taiga, the Arctic Fringe, Baikalia, the Lena Taiga,

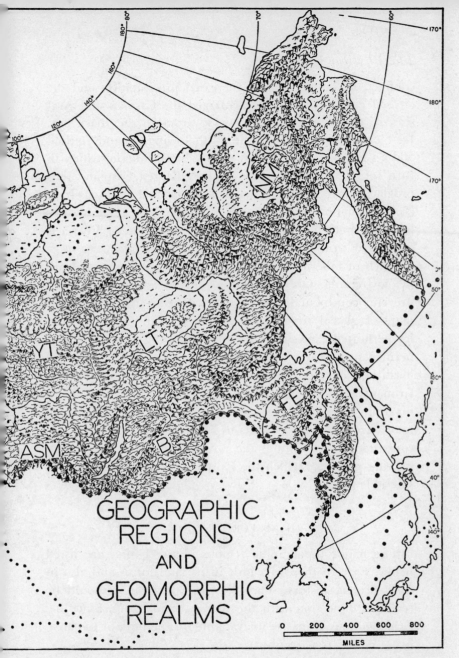

GEOGRAPHIC
REGIONS
AND
GEOMORPHIC
REALMS

Soviet Europe is divided into Ukrainia, White Russia, and Baltic States, the Central Agricultural Region, Metropolitan Moscow, the Southern Agri-aucasia, the Caspian Desert, the Pamirs and associated ranges, the Oases of of the West Siberian Agricultural Region, the Altai-Sayan Mountains, the the Northeastern Mountains, and the Far East.

(Drawn by William Black)

confined to the ice limits. Increased precipitation and decreased evaporation greatly enlarged the Caspian and Aral seas, so that they overflowed westward into the Black Sea. Ice blocked the mouths of the north-flowing Ob and Yenisei, and a vast lake developed in southwestern Siberia, which in turn found its outlet south to the enlarged Caspian. This proglacial lake exceeded the size of glacial Lake Agassiz in North America and was evidently the largest fresh-water lake ever known. The amazing flatness of western Siberia is due partly to the silt deposited by this huge lake.

Much of Siberia now has an average annual temperature below freezing. Only the absence of an adequate snowfall prevents continental glaciers today. During the rigorous climate of glacial times, the absence of blanketing snow or ice permitted excessive radiation so that the ground became permanently frozen. Extensive research, spread over 400 localities, has traced the characteristics of this frozen ground. In many areas it extends to depths of 100 feet and reaches a maximum of 920 feet. The total area underlain by permanently frozen earth amounts to 3,728,900 square miles. The construction of buildings and railroads presents special engineering problems which the Russians have solved with considerable ingenuity.

LAND FORM REGIONS

The major topographic regions of the Union are listed below. Each of these is a unit in its land forms and also in its structural history. The following paragraphs should be read in connection with the map of land forms. Since detailed contour maps are unavailable for the bulk of the area, many details remain obscure (see pages 72-73).

The list of regions and subregions follows.

A. Fenno-Scandian Uplands	Karelian Hills
	Kola Hills
B. Central European Lowlands	Baltic Glacial Plain
	Upper Dnieper Plain
	Pripet Marshes
C. Central Russian Uplands	Valdai Hills
	Smolensk-Moscow Hills
	Kursk Hills
D. Ukrainian Uplands	Don Hills
	Donets Hills
	Dnieper Hills
	Bug Hills
	Podolian Hills
	Dniester Hills
E. Central Russian Lowlands	Oka-Don Plain
	Upper Volga Plain
	Trans-Volga Plain
	Dvina Plain
	Pechora Plain
F. Volga Uplands	Pre-Volga Hills
	Ergeni Hills
G. Black Sea Lowlands	Lower Dnieper Plain
	Crimean Plain
	Kuban-Manych Plain
H. Ural Uplands	Ural Mountains
	Mogudjar Hills
	Nova Zemlya Hills
	Ufa Hills
	Timan Hills
	Ural Piedmont
I. Caucasian Highlands	Stavropol Foothills
	Greater Caucasus Mountains
	Mid-Caucasian Valleys
	Lesser Caucasus Mountains
	Crimean Mountains
J. Turan Lowlands	Caspian Depression
	Ust Urt Plateau
	Kara Kum Plain
	Kizil Kum Plain
	Hunger Plain

J. Turan Lowlands (*Cont.*)   Balkhash Basin
                                 Turgai Plain
K. Central Asiatic Highlands   Pamir Ranges
                                 Fergana Basin
                                 Tien Shan Ranges
L. Kazakh Upland
M. Altai-Sayan Highlands   Tarbagatai Mountains
                                 Siberian Altai Mountains
                                 Salair Mountains
                                 Kuznets Basin
                                 Kuznets Alatau Mountains
                                 Minusinsk Basin
                                 Western Sayan Mountains
                                 Eastern Sayan Mountains
N. West Siberian Lowland   Yamal and Gydan Peninsulas
                                 Ob Glacial Plain
                                 Vasyugan Swamp
                                 Ob Plain
                                 Khatanga Plain
O. Central Siberian Uplands   Anabar Hills
                                 Taimyr Peninsula
                                 Tunguska Hills
                                 Yenisei Ridge
                                 Vilui Plain
                                 Aldan Hills
                                 Patom Plateau
                                 Lena Hills
P. Baikal-Stanovoi Highlands   Baikal Mountains
                                 Vitim Plateau
                                 Yablonovi Mountains
                                 Olekminsk-Stanovik Mountains
                                 Stanovoi Mountains
Q. Far Eastern Uplands   Amur Basins
                                 Northern Amur Hills
                                 Sikhota Alin Mountains
                                 Sakhalin Island
R. Northeastern Mountain   Verkhoyansk Range
    Complex   Yana-Oimekon Lowlands
                                 Cherski Range
                                 Kolyma Lowlands

R. Northeastern Mountain   Okhotsk-Chaun Uplands
      Complex (*Cont.*)   Anadyr Mountains
                            Anadyr Lowlands
                            Kamchatka-Koryak Ranges

A. The Fenno-Scandian or Baltic Upland within the U.S.S.R. is a land of low hills developed on Pre-Cambrian rocks of great complexity. Glacial erosion has scoured and smoothed the surface, disrupted drainage, and produced innumerable lakes. Karelia resembles Finland. The Kola Peninsula is nearly detached and more mountainous. Along the eastern and southern margins is a series of depressions between the crystallines and bordering sedimentary rocks, due partly to glacial scour. This is represented by the Gulf of Finland and the White Sea at either ends and Lake Ladoga and Lake Onega in the center.

B. The Central European Lowlands include large areas west of the Soviet Union, extending into Germany and France, but within its limits are three separate regions. The Baltic Plain is the result of glacial deposition in a region of early Paleozoic sedimentaries. This region roughly coincides with the limits of Baltic drainage and the extent of the latest glacial invasion, the Wurm. It is crossed by a series of recessional moraines. The Upper Dnieper Plain was also glaciated but is a southward-sloping surface without lakes. The Pripet or Polesian Marshes spread over western White Russia into former Poland. The large extent of uncultivable land is reflected in the map of population density.

C. The Central Russian Uplands are a linear region of low hills. In the north the Valdai Hills are formed by a west-facing Devonian escarpment. The transverse Smolensk-Moscow Hills, which die out just north of Moscow, are in part a morainic belt. The southern and largest region is named the Kursk Hills from its principal city, better known for the presence of extensive iron ore deposits in the buried Voronezh crystalline block.

D. Beneath the Ukrainian Uplands is a partly exposed Pre-Cambrian Shield, but the topography is related to southward-dipping sedimentary formations of the late Paleozoic. These form a series of northwest-southeast cuestas arranged *en échelon.* Several Ukrainian rivers flow southeast, parallel to these escarpments, then turn and cut through them in valleys that predate the uplift of the hills. Hence reading from the east, the regions may be termed the Don Hills, the Donets Hills, famous for their coal, the Dnieper Hills, and the Bug Hills. Farther west are the Podolian Hills along the base of the Carpathians; these also have a north-facing escarpment overlooking the Pripet Marshes. Bessarabia might be included as the Dniester Hills, though the structural parallel does not hold.

E. The Central Russian Lowlands spread from the Arctic tundra to the southern black-soil steppes. The most representative region is the rolling hill and valley country south of Moscow drained by the headwaters of the Oka and Don. The Upper Volga Plain is slightly more hilly but still in its gross aspects a nearly featureless plain. Russians have long named various areas with relation to their position as regards Moscow, as for example the Trans-Volga Plain on the left bank below the junction of the Kama. This is a dry steppe which gradually rises to the Urals. Two regions of Arctic drainage complete the division, the Dvina Plain and the Pechora Plain. Both have a veneer of glacial deposits and postglacial marine sands. The Pechora area is underlain by coal and oil.

F. The Volga Uplands comprise the Pre-Volga Hills along the right bank, including the low Jiguli Mountains in the Samara Bend. The Ergeni Hills form the southern end of the area.

G. The Black Sea Lowlands include the Lower Dnieper Plain, extending from the Dniester to the Sea of Azov, the Crimean Plain in the northern two-thirds of the peninsula, and the extensive region between the Don and the Caucasus drained by the Kuban and Manych rivers. This was once an outlet for the enlarged Caspian Sea.

H. The Ural Uplands are an old mountain range, largely reduced to rounded hills. In history, structure, and relief they somewhat resemble the Appalachians. On the east is an abraded crystalline platform termed the Ural Piedmont. In the center are the narrow Ural Mountains proper, composed of folded geosynclines on either side of a granite core, deformed at the end of the Paleozoic. The southern projection is the Mogudjar Hills, and the northern extension is found in the islands of Nova Zemlya. The Timan Hills to the northwest are a peneplained anticline of late Paleozoic rocks, bordered by Mesozoic synclines. To the west of the Ural Mountains is a broad dissected plateau carved in Permian formations, the Ufa Hills.

I. The Caucasus presents great topographic variety, and the division here suggested is an oversimplification. On the north the Stavropol Foothills project into the Kuban-Manych Plain. Next is the main range of the Greater Caucasus, with rugged land forms and elevations to 18,468 feet. South of the mountains are valleys draining toward the Black and Caspian seas, and beyond them rise the Lesser Caucasus Mountains followed by portions of the high Armenian Plateau. The structure of the Greater Caucasus is continued in the mountains of southern Crimea.

J. The Turan or Central Asian Lowland is mostly desert. The Caspian Depression embraces the area north of the sea, partly below ocean level, which was covered when the enlarged Caspian overflowed westward. East of the Caspian is the Ust Urt Plateau. Three desert plains lie between and on either side of the Amu Darya and Syr Darya. Between the former and the Caspian is the Kara Kum, sometimes romanized as Qara Qum; between the rivers is the Kizil Kum or Qizil Qum, and to the east of the Syr Darya is the Hunger Plain or Bedpak Dala. The Balkhash Basin farther east commands the entrances to China. The Turgai Plain in the north is a corridor into Siberia and once carried drainage from glacial lakes to the north.

K. The Central Asiatic Highlands mark the structural core of the continent and extend into Afghanistan, India, and China. The Pamir region includes numerous other mountains such as the Alai, Turkestan, and Gissar. Here are the highest elevations in the Soviet Union: Mt. Stalin, 24,-584 feet, and Mt. Lenin, 22,377 feet. North of these ranges is the Fergana Basin in the upper valley of the Syr Darya. Beyond it is the western end of the Tien Shan with numerous subregions.

L. The Kazakh Upland is an ancient mountain range, worn down to rolling hills and plains so that only the roots of the mountains remain. Coal and copper are important. This area has sometimes incorrectly been called the Kirghiz Steppe.

M. The southern and eastern borders of Siberia are fringed with high mountains, from the Altai to the Verkhoyansk. The Altai-Sayan Highlands are made up of numerous structures with a general northwest-southeast trend. At the western end are the Tarbagatai Mountains, and next to them the Siberian Altai which continue into Mongolia. The Salair and Kuznets Alatau extend northward on either side of the Kuznets Basin, famous for its coal. East of the Kuznets Alatau is the Minusinsk Basin along the upper Yenisei, surrounded on the south side by the Western Sayan and on the north by the Eastern Sayan. The latter extends to near Lake Baikal.

N. The West Siberian Lowland occupies the vast plain of the Ob and Irtysh, one of the largest and flattest regions on earth. Two peninsulas characterize the Arctic portion, the Yamal and Gydan. The northern Ob Plain is veneered with glacial and recent marine deposits; south of it is the Vasyugan Swamp. Along the Trans-Siberian Railway is a dry plain, pitted with innumerable deflation hollows. It is drained by the Tobol, Ishim, Irtysh, and Ob rivers. The Khatanga Plain is a northeast continuation of the Lowland. The Lowland extends a short distance to the east of the Yenisei.

O. The Central Siberian Uplands reach from the Yenisei to the Lena and are sometimes called Angara land. The core is the Anabar Hills, or Shield, north of the Tunguska Hills, a dissected platform of late Paleozoic formations with extensive coal beds and widespread lava flows. The Taimyr Peninsula projects into the Arctic beyond the Khatanga Plain. In the southwest, a ridge along the Yenisei combines with the Eastern Sayan and Baikal Mountains to enclose the amphitheater of Irkutsk, a southern subdivision of the Tunguska platform. The geomorphic characteristics of the Lena Valley are less apparent. A large basin in the center may be termed the Vilui Plain, and in the south are the Patom and Aldan plateaus, the latter a shield. The remainder of the valley is grouped as the Lena Hills; part of the region is a plain.

P. The Baikal-Stanovoi Highlands continue the mountainous relief described in the Altai-Sayan Highlands. The Baikal Mountains rise on either side of the graben that holds the lake. To the east is the Vitim Plateau, part of the ancient shield of southeastern Siberia, and beyond it are the Yablonovi Mountains. These have a southwest-northeast trend and extend from the Mongolian border to the Olekma River. East of them is an area of low mountains and basins known as the Olekminsk-Stanovik Mountains. Much uncertainty has surrounded the use of the word Stanovoi, but it is now clear that it embraces a series of mountains from near the upper end of Lake Baikal eastward and northward along the Okhotsk Sea to latitude 60°.

Q. The Far Eastern Uplands include but one well-defined mountain chain, the Sikhota Alin. The remaining geomorphology is obscure. A series of basins along the Amur and its tributaries, notably the Zeya, Bureya, and Ussuri, form the chief plains. The island of Sakhalin may be included.

R. The Northeastern Mountain Complex is adequately characterized by its title. The line of the Stanovoi is continued by the curving Verkhoyansk Range along the right bank of the Lena. Between it and the high Cherski Range are the Yana and Oimekon Lowlands; air drainage into these basins makes them the coldest inhabited places on earth. The Kolyma Lowlands comprise the swampy Kolyma Plain in the north, the Alazeya Plateau on the west, and the Yukagir Plateau on the south. Farther east and south is a series of uplands, chief of which is the Gydan Range bordering the northern Sea of Okhotsk and continuing through the Anyui Mountains to the Arctic. The Anadyr Mountains cover the Chukchee or Chukotsk Peninsula opposite Alaska, and the Anadyr Lowlands lie between the Anadyr and Gydan Mountains and the Koryak Mountains. The peninsula of Kamchatka contains volcanoes whose size and activity parallel those of Java.

CLIMATIC CHARACTERISTICS

Despite the vast extent of the Soviet Union, climatic conditions over a large part of the country have much in common. The situation is different near the Black Sea, across the Caspian, and in the Far East, but elsewhere long winters and low precipitation dominate (see pages 74-75).

Millions of square miles are eliminated from normal settlement because of too short a growing season or too little rainfall. Elsewhere, occasional frosts that extend into the summer or come early in the fall, the lack of adequate spring rainfall or ground moisture from melting snow, or drying winds introduce crop uncertainties that do not appear in the annual statistical averages.

It has long been a recognized climatic rule that the lower the average annual rainfall, the greater the variability from year to year. It appears to be equally true that the lower the annual temperature, the greater the variation in the period between spring and fall frosts. Climatic hazards thus compress the central fertile triangle on both north and south.

Only a few areas in the west and in the higher mountains receive more than 20 inches of rainfall. If it were not for the low summer temperatures and limited evaporation, almost none of the country would be safe for agriculture. Middle Asia and northeastern Siberia each have under eight inches, but where the former is hot and a desert, the latter is cold and a tundra. Fortunately, precipitation in the cultivated areas comes during the summer when it is most needed, although the spring rains necessary for planting are often seriously delayed. Severe famines have resulted from this cause in the steppes of the Ukraine, Don, and Volga. During dry seasons the Emba does not reach the Caspian Sea, and streams in Kazakhstan run salty.

Although surrounded by seas, the country receives surprisingly little marine benefit. On the south, mountain barriers and great distances effectively bar any influence from the Indian Ocean. The Pacific lies to leeward on the wrong side of the continent, and mountains limit the penetration of summer monsoon moisture to Lake Baikal. For much of the year the Arctic Ocean is frozen, and the area of ice-free water as a source for evaporation is never large. Its low temperatures at all seasons make it an unimportant source of moisture or ameliorating warmth. Only the Atlantic remains, and it lies across the width of peninsular Europe; yet even in central Siberia more than three-quarters of the rain must be of Atlantic origin. While lowlands are dry, mountains such as the Sayan are unexpectedly moist, with a yearly precipitation of 47 inches. Apparently this moisture has come overland 4,000 miles from the Atlantic. This is all the more surprising since the only low altitude path from the Atlantic lies through the 900-mile gap between the Alps and the Scandinavian Highlands.

Changes of latitude and altitude do not always bring the normal results found elsewhere. The yearly average at Moscow is 3° F. lower than Leningrad, though 400 miles to the south, and winters in the deltas of the Volga and Syr Darya are colder than the Gulf of Finland. Likewise, the New Siberian Islands in the Arctic Ocean are warmer than the coast of Siberia, which in turn is warmer than the interior. There is thus the curious situation that a north wind brings warmer weather. In the same manner, the lowest recorded temperatures in the Yenisei Valley lie near the Mongolian border instead of at the mouth, 1,300 miles to the north. Stations on the Sea of Azov have the same January average as the northern coast of the Kola Peninsula.

Air drainage in the mountains introduces further inversions. Intense winter radiation, especially in windless northeastern Siberia, causes cold air to flow into the valleys which become colder than surrounding mountains. The extremely low temperatures at Verkhoyansk and Oimekon are well known with a January average of −59° F. and an extreme minimum of −90° F. at the former station. Even lower temperatures have been reported from Oimekon, where there is an unconfirmed reading of −103° F. and the annual average is apparently lower than at Verkhoyansk. These are the coldest towns in the world.

Winter is the dominant season. The frost-free period is less than 60 days in the Siberian Arctic and only 90 to 120 days in the northern half of Soviet Europe and central Siberia. In the central European area and the Ukraine and in southwestern Siberia, the frost-free time is between 120 and 180 days, and exceeds 200 days only in Middle Asia. Snowfall is not heavy but, since thaws are rare in winter, it accumulates and may be blown into formidable drifts. Throughout Siberia snow lies on the ground for 160 to 260 days, and in the European part of the Union it persists for 100 to 200 days except in the Ukraine.

The severity and duration of the winter season affect man in many ways. Daylight hours are short. Outdoor farm activities and general construction are obviously restricted. Blizzards block communications and cause the loss of unprotected cattle even as far south as the Ukraine. Fresh foods are lacking, and the winter diet is characteristically monotonous and deficient in vitamins.

Seasonal contrasts are intensified toward the east, and the range from January to July averages increases from 54° F. at Moscow to 119° F. at Verkhoyansk. This is shown in the table on page 98.

Summers are almost everywhere warm, with July isotherms extending east and west. Along the Arctic Coast long hours of sunshine raise the day and night monthly average to 50° F.; from Arkhangelsk and Igarka south to Kiev and Irkutsk, July temperatures are 60 to 68° F.; in the steppes temperatures increase to 75° F. and exceed that in the deserts.

January conditions show no east-west uniformity; instead the isotherms are from northwest to southeast. Monthly averages in Soviet Europe are from 25 to 5° F., while Siberian

CLIMATIC DATA

	Average Jan. temp., °F.	Lowest Jan. temp., °F.	Average July temp., °F.	Highest July temp., °F.	Average annual temp., °F.	Average annual precipitation, in.
Leningrad...........	15.3	−35	63.9	97	38.7	18.8
Moscow.............	12.2	−44	66.0	99	39.0	21.0
Kazan..............	7.2		67.5		37.4	15.4
Saratov.............	11.5		72.1		42.1	14.9
Baku...............	38.1		28.8		57.9	9.5
Batumi.............	43.0	18	73.4	95	57.7	93.3
Tashkent...........	30.0	−15	80.8	109		14.0
Tomsk..............	−3.3	−60	65.7	95	30.2	19.9
Irkutsk.............	−5.4		65.1		31.3	14.5
Yakutsk............	−45.9	−84	66.2	102	12.2	13.7
Verkhoyansk........	−58.9	−90	59.7	93	2.7	3.9
Vladivostok.........	4.8		66.0		39.7	14.7

stations drop to −5° F. or even −40° F. Soviet Middle Asia has averages of 32 to 14° F.

During winter, great masses of cold air develop in the vicinity of Lake Baikal and westward along latitude 50° N., with high pressure averaging 30.5 inches. This stationary center of Subpolar Continental air is the dominant factor in winter climate, with outblowing winds over most of Asia. Winter winds over western Siberia and Europe, however, tend to blow from the south and southwest. Summer conditions are not entirely reversed, for solar insolation moves the center of low pressure to Mongolia and northwestern India. Summer circulation is irregular, but in general there are inblowing winds from the west and northwest from the Atlantic.

Cyclonic storms introduce variations at all seasons. Their paths across western Europe are well known, but less information has been available concerning their movements into Asia. Meteorological stations are now widespread in

Siberia, and the Soviets issue daily weather maps of the entire Northern Hemisphere. Examination of the maps for February, 1936, shows that eleven highs and seven lows moved eastward across the Yenisei between the Mongolian border and the North Pole. In August, 1936, the same area was crossed by seven highs and five lows. Although their intensity is less, this is no fewer than the number of cyclonic and anticyclonic storms that cross Europe. Siberian weather is less monotonous than sometimes regarded.

NATURAL VEGETATION

The major pattern of natural vegetation is both simple and significant. No other regional picture is so expressive of land usability, for natural vegetation sums up many of the items of temperature, rainfall, surface configuration, drainage, and soils. In long-settled lands such as China, man has so changed the landscape that the original cover of vegetation is gone, but in undeveloped areas like Siberia it still dominates (see pages 76-77).

Most of the Soviet Union is a forest land, a fifth of that on earth. Many of the trees are conifers such as pine, spruce, or larch; and broad-leaved forms are in many places softwoods like birch and aspen. Oak and other hardwood forests were never extensive and are now largely cut over. Most furniture is perforce made of softwoods. Pine railroad ties deteriorate within five years unless treated.

If one might look down on the country from a height great enough to see all of it at a glance, the major zones of vegetation would stand out as belts of color, irregularly extending from west to east. Just south of the Arctic Ocean lies the tundra, a treeless land of lichens, moss, and low brush. Dull greens are occasionally relieved by the white bark of stunted birch. During the summer there is a short-lived period of verdant grass and brilliant flowers.

Farther from the ocean is the vast coniferous forest, the taiga. Here the dark greens of the pine, spruce, and larch are relieved by patches of whitewoods, such as birch and aspen, but the effect is somber and monotonous. Swamps spread over vast areas in both tundra and taiga. The greatest play of colors is found along the southern margins of the taiga in the Ukraine and along the Amur where stands of broad-leafed hardwoods are mixed with the coniferous softwoods. Here, bright summer greens and brilliant fall foliage are interspersed with meadows.

Where moisture drops below the minimum for trees, the forest gives way to grasslands in the steppe. These boundless plains have stamped their personality on the southern third of the country. These grasslands rarely have the lush greenness of the American prairie; rather they are pale green in the summer when grass attains a height of two feet or more and turn brown in autumn.

Where rainfall is still less, most vegetation disappears and the observer sees shifting reddish sands, yellowish loess, and bare rock. Even deserts display flashes of green and brilliant carpets of flowers after transient showers.

The distribution of vegetation is best understood if lowland landscapes with their horizontal zones are distinguished from vertical zonation in the mountains. They are accordingly considered first.

The tundra has a severe winter with frosts even in summer. From north to south are four subzones, the first of which is the Arctic tundra with moss and lichens but without trees or bushes. Second is the typical bush tundra with dwarf birch and willow, widespread lichens, and moss. Next is the south tundra with low fir, birch, and larch trees along river valleys, and well-developed sphagnum peat bogs. The wooded tundra, the fourth subzone, forms a transition to the true forest. Patches of tundra are present almost to the southern limit of the taiga, but in general the tundra zone lies north of the Arctic Circle and within 250 miles of the ocean. The southern limit corresponds with the July isotherm of 50° F.

Tundra vegetation is exclusively perennial. Many forms spread over the ground to secure the maximum insolation. Dwarf growths are typical. Bright flowers and green grass suddenly come to life during the long summer days. Remains of trees in peat bogs more than 100 miles north of the present wooded tundra suggest a warmer and drier post-glacial climate. Since frozen subsoil prevents ground-water drainage, widespread swamps develop during the summer and become breeding grounds for swarms of mosquitoes.

Farther from the ocean is the taiga, a cool temperate forest, dominantly coniferous. Winters are severe, but summer months have average temperatures between 50 and 68° F. The usual trees are pine, fir, larch, and cedar, with subordinate but locally important areas of birch, aspen, and alder. There are scattered meadows on river flood plains and open watersheds.

East of Lake Baikal, Daurian larch replaces the Siberian larch which grows to the west and is especially adapted to growth above frozen ground. Where the soil is sandy and the blanket of vegetation is thin, summer thaw may reach a depth of six to ten feet, but where there is a blanket of moss and decaying vegetation, the thaw may penetrate no more than two or three feet. When the forest is burned, birch and whitewoods precede conifers in order of natural restoration. Peat bogs and marsh, widespread in western Siberia and northern Europe, are rare east of the Yenisei where relief is greater, the summers have less rainfall, and the air is dry. Much of the northern taiga has no commercial value, but trees are taller and larger in diameter toward the south. Large mammals such as elk, reindeer, bear, and lynx were formerly abundant, but the chief taiga animals are now rodents like squirrel, rabbit, and fox.

The mixed forest zone of the western Soviet Union lies in a milder climate where fir and oak are found together. The warmest month exceeds 68° F. Along river valleys such as the Volga, oak extends north to 57° N. The distribution of deciduous trees is somewhat conformable with the wedge of population and cultivated land. Oak forests spread from Leningrad almost to the Black Sea and east to the Ural and Kama rivers, bordering the Ural Mountains. Maple has about the same distribution; ash covers a smaller area; linden spreads farther north and east than oak, while hornbeam is confined to the middle Dnieper Valley. In the Far East, another mixed forest zone reappears in the basin of the Amur with oak, maple, ash, linden, and elm. Considerable areas of splendid timber remain. Bright summer greens and brilliant fall foliage distinguish these mixed forests from the somber taiga. The fauna includes wild boars, reindeer, leopards, and Manchurian tigers.

South of the continuous forest lies a transition zone termed the wooded steppe, where solid stands of trees alternate with open grassland. Local factors of soil, relief, or vegetation history cause islands of steppe to lie within the mixed forest, and forest outliers are present within the continuous steppe to the south. In the European areas, oak is dominant; in Siberia birch is the typical tree. In the west, the northern and southern boundaries are Kiev and Kharkov, respectively; along the Volga they are Kazan and Kuibyshev. East of the Urals the center of the wooded steppe follows the Trans-Siberian Railway from Chelyabinsk to Omsk and Novosibirsk.

The steppe is a treeless expanse with a continuous cover

of short grass, often developed on loessial soils. Summers are dry and warm, with the July average above 68° F.; the yearly rainfall is 12 to 16 inches. Only near the forest is the grass luxuriant enough to be termed a meadow; elsewhere cereal grass and feather grass are typical. The presence of chernozem soil shows that the absence of trees is not due to deforestation by man. Instead, the prolonged dry period, low summer humidity, and deep ground-water surface make natural forest growth unlikely. Shelter-belt planting has long been practiced in the European steppe, but the forests do not reproduce themselves.[1] In the Rostov oblast alone, these cover 75,000 acres.

The steppe zone continues from the Black Sea and northern Caucasus east to the Altai Mountains. Prominent steppe cities are Odessa, Rostov, Chkalov, formerly Orenburg, and Semipalatinsk. These grasslands are the traditional home of the Cossacks, especially in the valleys of the Don and Volga, and were once overrun by the Mongol hordes. The steppe has so stamped its personality on the southern third of the country that one author has facetiously entitled a volume "Across Russia, Steppe by Steppe."

The semidesert zone is another transition area. Whereas the steppe has a continuous cover of grass and in the true desert it is wholly absent, the semidesert has spotty vegetation. Rainfall is six to ten inches, and July temperature averages exceed 75° F. Characteristic plant forms are wormwood and cereal grass. Salt marshes are present.

The temperate deserts of the U.S.S.R. have hot and nearly rainless summers, with July averages to 85° F., and frosty winters. Annual evaporation from free water surfaces is ten times the precipitation, but soil moisture is locally main-

[1] Vyssotsky, G. N., Shelterbelts in the Steppes of Russia, *Journal of Forestry*, XXXIII (1935), 781-788.

Mirov, N. T., Two Centuries of Afforestation and Shelterbelt Planting on the Russian Steppes, *Journal of Forestry*, XXXIII (1935), 971-973.

tained by rivers from the snow-clad Pamirs. The deserts from the Caspian Sea to beyond Lake Balkhash are underlain by shifting sands and alkali soils. Vegetation is zoned according to rainfall, ground water, and salinity of the soil. Wormwood or sage is common in the north. All plants are especially adapted to reduce transpiration. Thickets of saxaul bushes have developed locally. During spring rains, ephemeral grasses and flowers rapidly come to life. Poplar and tamarisk grow in some valleys. The marmot is the chief animal, especially adapted to the desert by summer hibernation.

Subtropical Mediterranean forests are confined to the eastern and western valleys of Transcaucasia. Winters are so mild that vegetation grows throughout the year, and precipitation makes possible a luxuriant growth of broadleaf trees, with an admixture of conifers. Oak, hornbeam, and beech are typical at the lower elevations. Alder thickets are found in marshy areas.

Mountains introduce vertical zones in addition to the lowland conditions just described, in some cases with successive vegetation types from deserts at their base through meadows, deciduous and then coniferous forests, and finally to alpine tundra at the summits. Thus altitude is reflected by vegetation in replica of latitude. This is especially noticeable in the Caucasus and Pamirs which are capped by permanent snow fields.

Mountain grasslands range from alpine meadows with abundant rainfall on windward slopes to steppe or semidesert in the rain shadow. Forests of the Caucasus are especially rich and varied. In the Altai, steppe vegetation covers the lower slopes to around 3,000 feet, above which is a taiga forest to 6,000 feet, followed by alpine meadows. The snow line lies at 9,000 feet. In the mountains of northeastern Siberia, Daurian larch is dominant, but east of the Kolyma

River mountain tundra covers much of the highlands. Drainage and soils differentiate this mountain tundra from the low-level tundra along the coast.

SOILS

Russian soil scientists have led the world in the classification of soils on the basis of environmental differences which place their stamp on the soil. Although geologists have been content to discuss soil as weathered limestone or granite, it is now recognized that mature soils, those which have remained undisturbed for some centuries, bear the impress of climate and vegetation superimposed on their original characteristics. Thus the parent material, whether stream alluvium, glacial deposits, or rock weathered *in situ,* acquires a definite profile through the action of ground water and vegetation.

In areas of abundant rainfall, soluble minerals are leached and removed in solution, while in arid regions such minerals remain in the soil. Where they are present to excess as in deserts, the soil becomes alkaline. Grass roots contribute more organic material to the soil than do the leaves of trees. Coniferous forests give rise to more acid soils than deciduous forests.

Across the Soviet Union, the major soil types reflect climatic and vegetation zones, as well as recent geologic history. Tundra vegetation is associated with tundra soils, the taiga is roughly coextensive with podsol soils, mixed forests coincide with brown forest soils, the steppe area has produced rich chernozem soils, the semiarid lands have chestnut-brown soil, and the desert corresponds with saline or alkaline soils.

Tundra soils are unfrozen for so little of the year, and

then have such limited drainage, that they seldom develop a mature profile. Decaying vegetation overlies the mineral soil and renders it so acid that cultivated crops can be raised only with special treatment.

Podsols cover nearly half of the Soviet Union. The typical profile shows a surface organic layer derived from coniferous trees, below it a sandy ash-colored horizon which gives the podsols their name, then a dark brownish clay-enriched zone, and below these the unaltered parent material. In the north, podsol formation is retarded by marshes, in the south by deficient moisture. Despite their acid character these podsols provide the soil for a third of the cultivated area. Similar soils are widespread in Canada.

The most productive soil in the world is the chernozem, more extensively developed in the U.S.S.R. than in any other country. It is a grassland soil, black with organic matter and high in lime and soluble plant foods. Some of it is developed on loess. But the very climatic factors that make this soil so fertile also make its agricultural utilization precarious, for rainfall is low and erratic. Were the rainfall heavier, forests would replace the steppe and there would be no chernozem soil. Chernozems occupy half the cultivated land; so long as the natural sod is not destroyed, wind erosion is seldom serious but, once the soil is cultivated, extensive deflation may take place. Dust-bowl erosion has long been critical in the Eurasian steppes. Chernozem soils are developed in a broad belt from the Ukraine to the Ob River. Whereas they extend from west to east in the Soviet Union, in the United States these soils occupy a north-south belt near the 100th meridian.

Chestnut-brown soils, moderately high in humus and very high in lime, lie in the semiarid lands of the south, while gray desert soils, often alkaline, cover the vicinity of the

Aral Sea. In dry lands where water plays a diminished role in soil formation, the parent material has added importance.

Irrigation may make the dry soils usable, but care must be taken for adequate subsurface drainage so that excess water does not evaporate to form a salty crust, known as an artificial solonchak.

5

SOVIET MINERAL WEALTH

THERE are few Soviet achievements of which the Russians are more proud than the charting of their vast mineral wealth, and deservedly so. It is now clear that the Union is one of the richest nations in the world, and that its coal, oil, iron, gold, potassium salts, and phosphate are of vast extent. However, not all Soviet mineral deposits are of high grade, or are easily accessible, or lie near the requisite fuel. Merely to locate a million tons of copper-bearing rock does not define an economically workable ore. Under a socialist or nationalistic regime it may be feasible to develop minerals with little regard to costs, but although the major picture is one of exceptional abundance, overoptimistic conclusions should not be drawn from a mere tabulation.

Economic life in the twentieth century rests fundamentally on agriculture and mining as the two great sources of primary production. Modern wars are largely a contest for these resources and for favorable living space in which to develop them. The Soviet Union is exceptionally fortunate in this regard, and the envy of her neighbors to the east and the west.

Geological studies date from the days of Peter the Great who established state mines in the Urals in 1699. With the development of the five-year plans came a great increase in field work, especially with relation to mineral deposits. In 1936, the Central Institute of Geology and Prospecting had a staff of 500 geologists and a budget of $2,300,000. Research has yielded large dividends, for many new mineral localities have been discovered and the boundaries of known deposits enlarged. During the period between the First and Second World Wars, the known reserves of coal increased sevenfold, of petroleum sevenfold, of zinc tenfold, of lead ninefold, of iron ore including ferriferous quartzites one hundred and thirty times, of copper twenty-eight times. Furthermore, vast resources of potassium, phosphate, and aluminum have been newly discovered.

POWER

Coal is the most important source of power, but in the Soviet Union wood for fuel comes ahead of petroleum. Even in 1925, many railway locomotives burned wood. From 1913 to 1937, the place occupied by coal rose from 60 to 70 per cent of all fuels, wood dropped from 22 to 12 per cent, petroleum declined from 17 to 12 per cent, and peat increased from 1 to 6 per cent.

In 1913 when the Twelfth International Geological Congress collected data on the coal reserves of the world, Russia was credited with 230,000,000,000 metric tons. At the Seventeenth Congress in 1937, Soviet reserves were placed at 1,-654,361,000,000 tons, easily second to the United States. These reserves are distributed through 83 fields from Moscow to Kamchatka, with nine-tenths of the tonnage in the Asiatic area. Bituminous coal amounts to 87 per cent.

The geology of coal is relatively simple, so that it is possible to estimate reserves with reasonable accuracy. Most of the world where coal is known to occur has been geologically surveyed and estimates of total coal resources may be made. For all the earth, these reach the incomprehensible total of over seven trillion tons. The world as a whole will not lack for coal for centuries. More than half of this vast total, some three and a half trillion tons, is within the United States. Not all is of top quality, for the estimates include great amounts of lignite in the Great Plains, but America easily leads all countries. The Soviet Union comes second with one and two-thirds trillion tons, largely bituminous of good quality. Canada comes third with about a trillion tons, largely low-grade lignite. China is in fourth place with a quarter of a trillion tons. No other power in Eurasia begins to compare with the Union in the extent of its undeveloped reserves; production, however, is another matter.

In the accompanying table, Soviet coal reserves are bituminous except as listed, and the areas where at least some of the coal is of coking quality are so indicated. The geological age is also indicated.

SOVIET COAL FIELDS

Mining Areas	Reserves in Millions of Metric Tons
Donets Coal Basin (Upper Carboniferous, anthracite and coking)...	88,872
North Slope Caucasus (Jurassic)	4,068
Georgia (Jurassic)	309
South Moscow (Lower Carboniferous, lignite)	12,400
Pechora (Permian)	±3,000
Western Urals (Lower Carboniferous)	4,777
Eastern Urals (Triassic, lignite)	2,872
Karaganda (Lower Carboniferous, coking)	52,696
Kuznets (Permian, coking)	450,658
Minusinsk (Permian)	20,612
Chulym-Yenisei (Jurassic, lignite)	43,000
Kansk (Jurassic, lignite)	42,000
Irkutsk and Transbaikalia (Jurassic)	81,397
Bureya	26,116
Suchan (coking)	42,000
Tunguska (Lower Carboniferous)	±400,000
Lena (Mesozoic)	±60,000
Total for U.S.S.R.	1,654,361

Coal production has steadily increased so that the Union occupies third place in Eurasia, preceded by Britain and Germany. Not only has tonnage increased but its distribution has changed. Prior to the First World War nearly nine-tenths of the output came from the Ukraine, but so great was the devastation of the area during the German invasion of the Second World War and so extensive was the development of mining in Siberia, that the Ukraine may never again produce half the total. The shift from Donets to Kuznets is shown in the accompanying table.

COAL PRODUCTION

Year	Total Soviet output, tons	Donets area		Kuznets area	
		Tonnage	Per cent	Tonnage	Per cent
1913	29,100,000	25,288,000	87	799,000	3
1928	35,500,000	27,330,000	77	2,743,000	8
1932	64,400,000	45,044,000	70	7,544,000	12
1934	93,500,000	61,496,000	65	11,974,000	13
1936	125,957,000	82,000,000	60	17,300,000	14
				(1937)	
1938	132,900,000	80,700,000		(20,000,000)	
				(25,000,000)	
1940	164,600,000				

Other fields with their production in thousands of tons for 1938, unless indicated, were as follows: the Urals, 8,100; Moscow, 7,400; the Far East, 4,700; Karaganda, 3,900; Irkutsk, 3,700 (1937); Kirghiz, 900; Trans-Caucasus, 500; Pechora, 120 (1937).

The Donets Coal Basin, whose name is often shortened to Donbas, lies north of the Black Sea and has always been the country's leading producer but, despite a threefold increase since 1913, its proportion of the national output has declined by a third, because of the rise of Kuznets and many new fields. The Donets coal fields have an area of 10,000 square miles, about three-quarters of which lies within the Ukrainian S.S.R. There are 2,000 shafts. Nearly half the coal is anthracite, but there are large amounts of bituminous coal suitable for metallurgical coke or chemical uses and gasification. The output supplies the blast furnaces based on the Krivoi Rog iron deposits, 200 miles to the west, as well as most railway and industrial needs west of the Urals.

Both north and south of Moscow are lignite areas which ranked third in production in 1937, with a yield of 7,750,000 tons. Much of the coal is used in central heat and power stations, where low-grade fuel may be efficiently burned in special furnaces. Both here and in the Donets area, there is some underground gasification of coal *in situ*. The air supply is controlled so that either high-calorie gas may be obtained for boilers, or "process" gas for synthetic benzine and ammonia.

The newly developed Pechora fields are near the Arctic Circle just west of the Urals. Production in the Vorkuta district supplies coal to Leningrad via a new railway. An annual output of 2,000,000 tons was planned by 1942. Farther south are deposits on the eastern and western slopes of the Urals. The western coals are high in sulphur and do not make suitable coke for blast furnaces, but they are usable for locomotives, electrical power, and for reducing sulphide copper ores. The principal mine is at Kizel, with an output of 3,000,000 tons. Much of the coal on the eastern side is lignite, such as deposits near Chelyabinsk, where production increased from 390,000 tons in 1925 to 3,519,000 tons in 1936. The combined output of the western and eastern Ural fields was 8,080,000 tons in 1937.

The development of the Kuznets Basin, sometimes called Kuzbas, has transformed a mid-Siberian steppe, south of the Trans-Siberian Railway, into a great industrial center. Reserves once estimated at 13,000,000,000 tons have been increased to 450,658,000,000 tons, and the annual capacity of the 50 operating collieries in 1937 was 17,300,000 tons. The output of the field is equal to nearly all that of India, or half of Japan. Great expansion occurred during the Second World War. With a high calorie content, combined with low ash and sulphur, the coals are the best in the Union. Anthracite accounts for 54 billion tons of the total reserve. Much of the output is used in the Ural-Kuznets metallurgical combine.

Between Kuznets and the Urals lie the newly surveyed and very important Karaganda coal fields. Their proximity to the Urals has caused them partly to replace Kuznets coal in the Magnitogorsk blast furnaces. The 1937 production reached 3,937,200 tons.

East of Kuznets are a number of partly developed coal fields. The Minusinsk Basin, where a few mines operate at Chernogorsk, lies on the Yenisei south of the Trans-Siberian Railway. The Chulym-Yenisei brown coal field extends north of Krasnoyarsk to the junction of the Angara and west along the railway to Mariinsk, but is undeveloped. East of the Yenisei is the Kansk brown coal area, also along the railway. West of Irkutsk, 3,000,000 tons of coal were mined in 1937 at Cheremkhovo, and the deposits continue east of Lake Baikal.

Important coal fields are present in the Amur Valley, especially along its tributary, the Bureya. Near Vladivostok, coking coal is mined at Artem, 2,110,000 tons in 1937, and at Suchan, 590,000 tons.

In the Yenisei and Lena valleys lie two vast coal regions, largely undeveloped. Deposits east of the Yenisei, at present worked only at Norilsk, are called the Tunguska Coal Field, after the three tributary Tunguska rivers. Deposits along the Lena are worked on a small scale at Sangar Khai. Sakhalin also produces coal. Coal is mined along the borders of the Caucasus and Pamirs.

Peat production has risen from 1,750,000 tons in 1913 to 26,500,000 tons in 1938.

Not only are Soviet coal reserves exceedingly large; they are also well distributed. The Urals lack proper metallurgical coke, but new developments at Karaganda make it unnecessary to bring fuel from Kuznets. Moscow, once dependent on Donets coal, now produces almost enough local lignite. Leningrad once used British or German coal but has developed large central plants for burning near-by peat.

The geology of oil and gas is more complicated than that of coal, so that reserves can only be generalizations. Soviet production has long been a poor second to the American, but her reserves may approach or exceed those of the United States. Data on petroleum resources in the U.S.S.R. as presented to the Seventeenth International Geological Congress are given in the accompanying table.

SOVIET OIL FIELDS

Localities	Metric Tons[1]
Apsheron Peninsula (Baku)	781,300,000
Other areas in Azerbaidzhan	1,771,000,000
Grozny	174,800,000
Maikop and vicinity	156,900,000
Georgia	176,200,000
Daghestan	146,000,000
Emba	1,190,400,000
Bashkiria (Sterlitamak)	365,200,000
Perm-Kama	354,000,000
Other West Urals and Volga	471,500,000
Sakhalin	339,800,000
Middle Asia	427,100,000
Total for U.S.S.R.	6,376,300,000

[1] One metric ton of petroleum is equal to 5 to 10 barrels of 42 gallons, according to specific gravity.

This vast total may be divided into various categories of probability, of which "proved and prospected" amount to 230,700,000 tons, and "visible" an additional 652,000,000 tons. The remainder is little more than an optimistic geological estimate. The comparative figure in the United States for these first two categories is 1,765,000,000 tons. Intensive geological and geophysical prospecting has located new fields

Peat has become an important fuel in the northern areas of Soviet Europe where local coal is not available. This scraper prepares peat in blocks for drying. (*Sovfoto*)

Scores of modern coal mines lie in the Donets fields of southern Ukrainia. This colliery is north of Rostov. (*Sovfoto*)

The world's largest deposits of apatite and nepheline occur in Khibin Mountain on the Kola Peninsula south of Murmansk. (*Sovfoto*)

A narrow-gauge railway leads from Dudinka on the Yenisei across the Arctic to the new mining town of Norilsk, shown above. (*Sovfoto*)

and spread production widely from the prerevolutionary center at Baku.

Production figures for the entire U.S.S.R. are as follows:

PETROLEUM OUTPUT

Year	Metric Tons
1901	11,000,000
1913	7,627,000
1920	2,915,000
1928	11,625,400
1932	21,413,200
1936	27,337,700 (from 45 operating fields)

In contrast to the widespread occurrence of coal, oil deposits are largely in a single zone, from the Caucasus and Caspian Sea north to the central Urals. Elsewhere, the far eastern island of Sakhalin is important; oil is produced in the Pechora Basin; and there is a small output at Nordvyk along the Siberian Arctic Coast, and in Kamchatka. The bulk of Siberia and Soviet Middle Asia appears to be without petroleum reserves.

Baku in the Azerbaidzhan Republic has always been far in the lead as a producer, and output dates from 1869. In 1901 it supplied half the world's output. Most of the production comes from Pliocene sands on the Apsheron Peninsula, but there are numerous horizons down to the Lower Cretaceous. Wells go to a depth of 8,648 feet. Two pipe lines lead south of the Caucasus to Batumi on the Black Sea.

The second producing district is along the northern slopes of the Caucasus in the vicinity of Grozny and Maikop. Large reserves of natural gas also occur in these areas.

Several pipe lines lead from the Caspian Sea to the Black Sea, and one continues northwest to the Donets Basin.

Northeast of the Caspian along the Emba River are at least 100 salt domes. In 1937 there was a production of 466,000 tons from 20 developed domes. Oil occurs in formations from the Permian to Paleocene. A pipe line from the

Caspian Sea leads through the Emba fields northwest to Orsk and eastward across Siberia.

The oil fields between the Volga and the southern Urals have been developed since 1928. Reserves here appear to be so extensive that the area is termed a "second Baku." Proved fields extend from the Caspian depression north to the Kama River.

Sakhalin is the chief producing area in the Far East. The 1936 yield in the Okha field amounted to 470,000 tons, of which a third was obtained by Japanese concessionaires. These concessions were terminated in 1943.

The third source of power is hydroelectric, and Soviet plans in this field are as ambitious as elsewhere. Only in the Caucasus, Pamirs, Tien Shan, and eastern Siberia are there swift streams fed by melting snow. Elsewhere gradients are gentle and the flow seasonal, but rivers as large as the Volga and Yenisei make the potential power impressive.

Estimates of water power based on stream flow available 50 per cent of the time amount to 280,690,000 kilowatts, while that available 95 per cent of the time is 58,000,000 kilowatts. The Lena system leads in potentialities, followed by the Yenisei and its tributary the Angara, the Far East, Soviet Middle Asia, the Ob, the Volga, the Caucasus, and Kola-Karelia. Most of these localities are remote from the present market for electricity.

An extensive program, initiated in 1920 under the direction of Lenin, calls for a series of coordinated stations on the Volga, the Dnieper, and in the Caucasus, supplemented by steam-operated plants in the Donets, Moscow, Leningrad, and Ural coal-producing areas. Subsequent plans provide for vast installations on the Yenisei south of Krasnoyarsk and especially on the Angara near Lake Baikal. The latter provides the base for one of the major industrial developments of the future, known as Angarastroi. Several projects are comparable to the Grand Coulee Dam on the Columbia River.

The proposed program is on a truly gigantic scale. Two dams under construction near Kuibyshev on the Volga will each generate over 1,000,000 kilowatts. On the Angara River, fed by the constant flow from Lake Baikal, there are eventually to be eight principal stations with a total capacity of 9,000,000 kilowatts. Four stations on the upper Yenisei will produce 4,000,000 kilowatts. Decades may elapse before these Siberian developments are completed, but the presence of near-by coal and iron makes large-scale industry possible.

The largest hydroelectric installation in Europe, and when built the largest in the world, was on the Dnieper River where it cuts through the Ukrainian Uplands at Zaporozhe. This had an installed capacity of 900,000 kilowatts when destroyed by the retreating Russians during the Second World War. The aggregate hydroelectric capacity of the Union in 1940 amounted to 2,500,000 kilowatts.

METALS

Iron is the indispensable material for construction. Reserves of iron ore were estimated in 1933 at 16,447,000,000 metric tons, of which actual reserves amounted to 9,238,000,-000 tons. These latter are further classified as brown limonite ore, 5,484 million; magnetite ore, 2,392 million; and red hematite ore, 1,571 million tons. Deposits are grouped in a few localities: the high-grade Krivoi Rog and inferior Kerch areas in the Ukraine and Crimea, the problematical ores of the Kursk magnetic anomaly, the brown ores south and east of Moscow, numerous occurrences in the Urals, notably the magnetite at Magnitogorsk and Nizhni Tagil, newly found deposits south of the Kuznets Basin and near Karaganda, undeveloped reserves along the Angara, and scattered deposits in the Far East. Large-scale production is more localized.

Krivoi Rog has long been the leading center of iron mining, although the Urals were discovered earlier. The ore is in Pre-Cambrian ferruginous chert and jaspellite, and is a banded mixture of hematite, altered martite, and magnetite, concentrated by hydrothermal weathering. In origin and problems it resembles the deposits near Lake Superior. The iron percentage in the martite averages 63 per cent, and in the hematite 51 per cent; these two make up three-quarters of the deposit. The magnetite and brown ores both carry 58 per cent iron. In 1937 there were 25 operating mines, one with a capacity of 6,000,000 tons and four others designed for 2,000,000 tons each. Reserves at Krivoi Rog aggregate 1,142,000,000 tons.

Ural iron has been known since 1702, and there are scores of localities. The largest development is at Magnitogorsk in the south, where large-scale operations started in 1931. The annual production at the beginning of the Second World War was 6,000,000 tons of ore. The ore is magnetite and secondary martite, formed by contact metamorphism, with a metallic content from 55 to 66 per cent. The oldest and second most important center is Nizhni Tagil, in the north. Total Ural reserves are placed at 1,390,607,000 tons, of which a third is limonite. Magnitogorsk accounts for 450,-000,000 tons.

South and east of Moscow, notably at Lipetsk and Tula, are sedimentary brown hematite ores of lacustrine and lagoon origin. Reserves total 424,000,000 tons.

Near Kerch at the eastern end of Crimea are deposits consisting of brown oölitic, manganiferous, and phosphatic ores of Pliocene age. Reserves are placed at 2,726,000,000 tons, but the metallic content is only 35 per cent iron.

When the Kuznets coal field was developed, no near-by

iron was known, but since 1930 sizable deposits of magnetite have been developed in the Gornaya Shoria Mountains to the south. The ore is formed by metasomatic replacement and is associated with skarn with an iron content of 45 per cent. Reserves in the Gornaya Shoria may reach 292,412,000 tons. Of similar importance are the ores found near Karaganda during the Second World War.

East of Lake Baikal ore is mined near Petrovsk-Zabaikal, and in the Amur Valley both near the mouth and in the Little Khingan Mountains.

The preceding deposits are all in production. Among undeveloped reserves, the outstanding is the Kursk magnetic anomaly between Moscow and Kharkov. Compass deviations here have been known since 1874, but high-grade hematite and siderite ores comparable in richness to Krivoi Rog were discovered only in 1931. Reserves listed as "actual" and "probable" amount to 250,000,000 tons, while the total may reach 6,000,000,000. This would make it one of the largest ore bodies on earth, but metallurgical difficulties make development problematical. Small but important ore deposits are in process of development on the Kola Peninsula. Iron is also found in the Caucasus and Pamirs. In eastern Siberia, the most important locality is along the Angara and Ilim rivers, northwest of Lake Baikal, where reserves are calculated at 420,850,000 tons.

The production of iron ore amounted to 9,300,000 metric tons in 1913; 8,000,000 in 1929; 14,500,000 in 1933; and 26,529,700 tons in 1938. In the latter year the Ukraine contributed 16,069,700 tons and the Urals 7,729,000 tons. Its utilization is considered in the next chapter.

Manganese is the most essential of all other ferrometals, since 14 pounds are required in the manufacture of each ton of steel. The Soviet Union leads the world in reserves, which were estimated at 700,000,000 tons in 1936, and in production, which exceeds 4,000,000 tons. The largest deposit is that of Nikopol in the southern Ukraine, but the ore at Chiatury in Georgia is of higher grade, largely mined for export. Manganese is also mined in the Urals, in Kazakhstan, and west of Krasnoyarsk. The Nikopol ore is a Tertiary laterite type deposit above Pre-Cambrian crystallines, 4 to 12 feet thick and buried by Quaternary sands.

Copper reserves were greatly enlarged by exploration during the five-year plans, but the quality of the ore is poor. Kazakhstan has the chief deposits, exceeding those of the Urals and the Caucasus. Many of the deposits contain less than two per cent copper, and their economic workability is questionable. Production in 1930 amounted to 34,105 metric tons, and in 1940 to 166,200 metric tons, still considerably below the country's requirements. The leading mine is at Kounrad near the north shore of Lake Balkhash, where there are low-grade porphyritic deposits. A new smelter has an annual capacity of 100,000 tons of metal. Farther west are the richer Djezkazgan deposits where the production is to be double that of Kounrad. The Urals were formerly the principal copper area, with numerous deposits of varied types, chiefly pyrite. Ore bodies are found over a distance of 500 miles from the largest mine at Krasnouralsk in the north to Orsk in the south.

Lead and zinc reserves represent 11 and 19 per cent of the world totals, respectively. Important areas are Dzhaudzhikau, formerly Ordzhonikidze, in northern Caucasia, Ridder in the Altai Mountains, Trans-Baikalia, and the Maritime Province. Lead production amounted to 44,000 tons in 1938, and zinc to 80,000 tons.

Aluminum was regarded as a deficit metal in czarist Russia because the known bauxite deposits were limited and too poor to work. The metal is now secured from unsatisfactory ores at Tikhvin east of Leningrad, from large deposits in the northern Urals at Kabakovsk, formerly Nadezhdinsk, and in the southern Urals at Kamensk. Huge nepheline deposits in the Kola Peninsula are also worked for aluminum. The oldest reduction plant is at Volkhov near Leningrad. Two plants are located near the Dnieper hydroelectric station, and another is at Kamensk. A larger plant began operation in 1939 near Kandalaksha in the Kola Peninsula. Despite inferior deposits, the Soviet Union is a major producer, ranking third in 1940 with an output of 54,900 tons and a much larger yield in sight.

Nickel is mined in the central and southern Urals, at Norilsk near the lower Yenisei, and in the Kola Peninsula. The output of 3,000 metric tons in 1938 was barely adequate for domestic needs, but enabled the Union to rank as a very poor third in world output, following Canada and New Caledonia.

Gold has long been known in Siberia and the Urals, both as placer and lode deposits.[1] No production figures are published, but conservative foreign estimates place the 1939 output at 4,500,000 ounces, as compared with 5,173,000 ounces in 1936. Optimistic estimates are nearly double these figures. The Union holds second place to the Union of South Africa, closely followed by Canada and the United States. The most important areas are along the Aldan and Kolyma rivers in Yakutia. Other mining centers are scattered through eastern Siberia, Soviet Middle Asia, the Urals, and the Caucasus.

Platinum production provides over a third of the world's supply, largely from ultrabasic rocks near Nizhni Tagil in the Urals, well known for a century. Chromium is obtained from low-grade ores in the Urals, with an annual yield in excess of 200,000 metric tons of chromite. This placed the U.S.S.R. in first place, ahead of Turkey and South Africa.

[1] See VON BERNEWITZ, M. W., Russia's Gold Production, U. S. Bureau of Mines, Mineral Trade Notes, May 20, 1936.

Tin is found east of Baikal and in Kazakhstan, but production is negligible. Tungsten is mined in the same general area.

NONMETALS

In addition to a wide variety of the usual nonmetallic minerals, the Soviet Union has fabulously large deposits of two uncommon substances: apatite and potassium salts. Each has been developed with dramatic rapidity. In both cases resources and production lead the world.

Apatite is a source of phosphate, secured rarely as mineral apatite but most frequently from phosphate limestone rock as in North Africa. Soviet deposits are located north of the Arctic Circle in the Khibin Mountains of the Kola Peninsula, and are a magmatic segregation from nepheline syenite. Near by is the new town of Kirovsk with a population of 50,000. Two million tons are mined yearly, yielding 1,000,000 tons of purified apatite and 500,000 tons of purified nepheline. Ore reserves are established at 2,000,000,000 tons. When visited by the International Geological Congress excursion of 1937, the mine was regarded as one of the industrial wonders of the world. The property was developed in eight years and there were 20 miles of underground galleries, fully electrified. Ordinary freight trains carry out the ore from the heart of the mountain. The high-grade fertilizers obtained from the apatite are of vital importance in Soviet agricultural expansion. From the nepheline are produced soda and aluminum.

Potash is secured at Solikamsk on the western slope of the northern Urals. Salt had been known for three centuries, but potassium and magnesium salts and bromine were not found until 1925. The annual production amounted to 1,800,000 tons in 1937. Reserves of potassium salts are estimated at 15,000,000,000 tons, and those of magnesium salts at 18,000,000,000 tons. In addition there are still larger deposits of common salt, unworked. Germany has previously been the world's leading potash producer.

Asbestos has been secured from Asbest in the Urals near Sverdlovsk since 1889. The fiber occurs in serpentinized peridotite as in Quebec and Rhodesia. Similar deposits are present in the Altai-Sayan Mountains. Ural reserves are estimated at 17,500,000 tons of fiber longer than 0.7 millimeter, and the production is more than adequate for all domestic needs. Much of the fiber is short, but the percentage of long fiber is reported to be greater than in Canada. The Union holds second place in world output, with a yield over 100,000 tons. Talc and soapstone deposits in the Urals are also enormous.

Magnesite occurs in large deposits near Sverdlovsk and Chelyabinsk. The annual output of 800,000 tons supplies domestic needs and provides a large export to western Europe. Austria occupies second place in magnesite production.

Industrial salt is available in abundance. There are deposits at Solikamsk, Emba, and the Donets Basin.

Gems and semiprecious stones have been secured from the Urals for centuries, including emerald, beryl, amethyst, topaz, and massive blocks of malachite. Kaolin production is centered in the Ukraine. Fire clays are present in the Moscow Coal Basin and in the Ukraine. Mercury is available in the Donets Basin and in the Urals.

SUMMARY

Mining is concentrated in a few districts, near the more densely settled areas or along the major railways. Productive areas reflect historical developments, transportation facilities, and markets rather than reserves. The Ukraine has coal, iron, and manganese. The Moscow area has inferior coal and iron. In the Kola Peninsula are spectacular deposits of potash and uncommon minerals. The Urals are a tremendous storehouse of natural wealth, perhaps the richest mountain range of their size on earth. Here are iron, gold, asbestos, potassium and magnesium salts, aluminum, chromium, nickel, copper, low-grade coal, and oil. The Caucasus have oil, manganese, lead, and zinc. Kazakhstan contains coal, copper, lead, and zinc. The Pamirs, Tien Shan, Altai, and Sayan are all mineralized, with conspicuous coal and iron in the Kuznets Basin. Eastern Siberia, still partly unexplored, has coal, gold, iron, and other minerals. Despite this imposing list, large areas are entirely without resources.

The industrial utilization of these resources will be considered in the next chapter, but a mere listing of resources discloses the exceptional natural wealth of this vast area. Intensive geological research has greatly increased the known reserves, even in long-studied areas. No other country has so great a variety of minerals, and only the United States is richer.

At the same time, it is well to note that among these many deposits are some low-grade ores, especially copper and aluminum, which have doubtful value if operated on a basis of strict capitalist accounting. Moreover, reserves and production need to be considered in terms of a country eight million square miles in area inhabited by 200 million people.

The Soviet mining industry is still engaged in catching up with the rest of the world, but the accelerated developments just before and during the Second World War indicate that the lag may not long persist.

6

INDUSTRIALIZATION IN THE SOVIET UNION

THE industrial task of the Soviet Union under the five-year plans was to overtake and surpass the capitalist world, especially the United States. When one considers the limited development of industry in 1913 and the fact that postwar production did not regain this level until 1926, the audacity of such a goal is obvious. Lenin once said that in terms of industry, old Russia was "four times worse than England, five times worse than Germany, ten times worse than America." Owing to the relatively self-contained character of Soviet expansion, it was little retarded by the world-wide depression of the early 1930's.

Any analysis of Soviet economic development must first consider the reliability of Soviet statistics. Unfortunately a complete check is out of the question, for the only figures available are those of the government. Actual production figures are often confused with planned production or are given as percentages of increase without stating the actual quantity involved. This use of percentages reaches a humorous climax in the annual statistics from an Arctic station where it was reported that 2 per cent of the men had married 50 per cent of the women, yet only one marriage was involved.

By 1938, the Soviet Union claimed to hold first place within Europe in total industrial output. This was undoubtedly true in oil, potash, phosphate, peat, trucks, and tractors, but not in electrical power, coal, steel, copper, aluminum, or cement. Immense strides have been made, but decades must pass before the cumulative results give the Soviet landscape an appearance of material abundance resembling western Europe. With the industrial index of 1913 set at 100, that of 1938 was 908.8.

In terms of 1937 output per person, Soviet pig-iron production amounted to a third that of Germany or half that of England. The per capita coal output was less than a quarter that of Germany or one-seventh that of England. Cement was but one-fifth the German-English average. Cotton textile production equaled a quarter of the English output per capita, while paper was but one-eighth that of Germany and England.

Czarist Russia was dominantly agricultural. Half of such manufacturing as there was centered in Moscow and Leningrad, where light industries such as textiles were the rule. The Ukraine and Urals accounted for a third of the total industrial output. Under the five-year plans, and particularly during the Second World War, the industrial center of gravity shifted eastward, almost to the Urals.

Many changes have taken place in the industrial geography. Cotton grown in central Asia was formerly shipped to Moscow for weaving but is now made into cloth in Tashkent. Kuznets and Magnitogorsk are examples of new steel centers for the Siberian market. Outlying industries are not limited to the production of raw materials but include chemical works, cement plants, food packing, and paper.

Soviet economic activities are characterized by extensive planning, in which natural resources are inventoried and industries located by geographic studies. These factories are then financed by government banks and controlled by various commissariats. Thus the planned economy rests on the evaluation of natural resources and can be wise only insofar as complete basic data are available. This does not mean that plans cannot be changed to account for new discoveries. The very expensive Ural-Kuznets combine, for example, originally based on deposits of iron and coal far removed from each other with resultant expensive long rail haulage, has now been revised in terms of recently discovered natural resources. Coal has been found halfway between at Karaganda and will largely replace Kuznets coal at Magnitogorsk. Modest reserves of iron ore have also been uncovered near Kuznets. Efficient planning is possible only when all factors are known in advance.

HEAVY INDUSTRY

Iron and steel were fundamental in the five-year plans. The output of pig iron rose from 4,200,000 tons in 1913 to 14,900,000 tons in 1940. Whereas the Ukraine was almost the only steel area prior to the First World War, expansion in the interwar period added huge plants in the Urals and central Siberia.

The southern Ukraine is an ideal production area, for in addition to near-by high-grade coking coal and rich iron ore, there are manganese and hydroelectric power. On account of its favorable geography it should remain the major metallurgical area, despite the devastation that occurred in connection with German occupation. Iron ore from Krivoi Rog is shipped 200 miles east to blast furnaces in the Donets coal field at Makeevka, Stalino, Ordzhonikidze, Voroshilovsk, Konstantinovka, Kramatorsk, and Krasni Sulin. Coal is also carried west to the ore mines at Krivoi Rog, as well as to furnaces en route at Zaporozhe and Dniepropetrovsk. East of the Donets coal fields there are steel mills at Stalingrad. In addition to this east-west movement, Donets coal is shipped south to Mariupol on the Sea of Azov where it meets iron ore from Kerch in eastern Crimea; there are also blast furnaces at Kerch. The Makeevka plant alone turned out 1,300,000 tons of pig iron in 1936. If the ores of the Kursk magnetic anomaly, 200 miles north of Donets coal, prove workable, still further expansion is possible.

South of Moscow pig iron and steel are produced on a modest scale at Lipetsk and Tula, and to the east are steel mills at Kulebaki and Vyksa. Moscow also has a steel mill without blast furnaces.

No less than 39 localities produce iron or steel in the Urals. Some of these are old and obsolete plants operating on charcoal, but none of them are comparable in size to new giant furnaces at Magnitogorsk and Nizhni Tagil. Coal is supplied from Kuznets and Karaganda, for the local Kizel coal is high in sulphur and does not make good coke, although a passable fuel is obtained by mixture with Kuznets coke. Chelyabinsk coal is lignite and suitable only for power. When built, Magnitogorsk was equipped with four blast furnaces each of 1,400 tons capacity, and two more have since been added. To convert this pig iron into steel there are 20 open-hearth furnaces. In what was virgin steppe around Magnet Mountain has grown a city of 145,870 people (1939). Magnitogorsk is said to rank next to Gary, Ind., as the second largest individual steel mill in the world. The extensive plant at Nizhni Tagil, designed to equal Kuznets by 1945, is closely followed by new works at Sverdlovsk. Other furnaces are at Chelyabinsk, Khalilovo, and Bakal. The Urals, with a vastly increased steel output and abundance of other metals, stand second to the Ukraine in industrial importance. The absence of local metallurgical coke is a problem, but the newly developed Karaganda coal field is only 600 miles distant.

Although the Kuznets coal field lies 1,417 miles east of Magnitogorsk via the Trans-Siberian Railway, the new direct line reduces this distance to 1,200 miles. When the Ural-

Kuznets combine was inaugurated, no nearer coal was known, and the expense of the rail haul, the longest in the world, was to be partly offset by constructing duplicate steel plants at each end. The furnaces at Stalinsk, formerly Kuznets, thus have a capacity comparable to those of Magnitogorsk. When visited by the author in 1937, the four blast furnaces were producing a total of 4,000 tons per day. Nearby iron ore in the Gornaya Shoria is gradually replacing that from the Urals, and the lower quality is offset by the cheaper transportation. The Ural-Kuznets metallurgical combine supplied more than a quarter of the nation's iron in 1936 and was to be expanded to a third by 1942.

East of Lake Baikal is an old iron and steel works at Petrovsk-Zabaikal. New mills are in operation at Komsomolsk on the lower Amur, using Bureya coal and Little Khingan ore. A steel mill came into operation at Tashkent in 1942.

Projected iron centers include the Transcaucasus and Kola Peninsula. Eventual possibilities in Siberia involve Minusinsk coal and near-by Abakan iron ore, and especially Cheremkhovo coal and Angara-Ilim iron ore, to be developed along with Angara water power.

Copper, aluminum, lead, and zinc are also vital in heavy industry. Geographic problems of bringing ore and fuel together are not so difficult in these cases. There has been a continuous effort to open new deposits and spread production widely.

Large-scale electrochemical works have developed around the Dnieper Dam in the Ukraine, and around smaller sources of water power in the Kola Peninsula and Caucasus, with plans for industries in the Urals and Tien Shan. Another chemical industry is east of the Caspian Sea on Kara-Bogaz Gulf, where mirabilite, or sodium sulphate, and other chemicals are extracted from sea water.

Railway equipment is produced in the Ukraine and Ural areas, especially locomotives in a huge plant at Voroshilovgrad, formerly Lugansk; and rolling stock at Dnieprodzerzinsk and Nizhni Tagil. The principal centers of general machine production are Moscow, Leningrad, and Kharkov, with mining machinery at Kramatorsk in the Donets area and Sverdlovsk in the Urals.

Agricultural machinery has received much emphasis, with tractor plants at Kharkov, Stalingrad, and Chelyabinsk. Harvesters and combines are made at Rostov-on-Don, Saratov, and Kirovo.

Wartime developments brought great changes in the type and location of Soviet industries. Many factories from the areas invaded by the Germans were dismantled and removed to the Urals, to central Siberia, and to Soviet Middle Asia. For reasons of future security and since this eastward trend is in line with pioneering needs, much of this migration will be permanent.

The building of river steamers has long been important, with shops on the Dnieper at Kiev, on the Volga at Gorki, and elsewhere. Ocean-going vessels are built at Nikolaevsk near Odessa and at Leningrad.

Heavy industry is far more developed west of the Volga than elsewhere. Leningrad stands in a corner by itself. The Moscow-Gorki region is very important, but the Donets-Kharkov-Nikolaevsk region is dominant. The Urals from Magnitogorsk through Sverdlovsk to Nizhni Tagil are a growing area, as are the Caucasus, the Tashkent area, the Kuznets Basin, and the Far East. But even more than indicated by population distribution or cultivated land, the industrial core of the Soviet Union has been west of longitude 45° E. The growth of outlying areas is conspicuous and will continue, but so far as heavy manufacturing was concerned

Magnitogorsk is the giant steel center of the Urals, developed because of local iron ore. (*Sovfoto*)

The steel mills at Kuznets are the major base for heavy industry in Siberia. Prior to the First Five-year Plan this was an empty steppe. (*Sovfoto*)

The Volga is the Union's busiest river. This is the water front at Stalingrad. (*Sovfoto*)

Many Soviet locomotives which operate in the drier areas are equipped with condensers to conserve steam. (*Sovfoto*)

prior to June 22, 1941, the essential area was bounded by Rostov-on-Don, Stalingrad, Gorki, and Leningrad; in short, west of the Volga.

OTHER INDUSTRY

Within the wide scope of light industry, it is possible to speak of only wood products, textiles, food, and new synthetic products. Lumbering is almost as widespread as the forests themselves. Wherever a railroad crosses a river flowing out of a forested area, there are sure to be sawmills. There are no large papermaking centers, but the mills are generally north of the Volga and Kama, especially near Gorki and Vologda, or in White Russia.

Cotton textile production is centered chiefly in the area bounded by Moscow, Ivanovo, and Yaroslavl. Leningrad and the Ukraine produce largely for local consumption. This grouping of mills has little geographic justification because they are remote from the cotton fields of Soviet Middle Asia, and the market is more widely spread. New mills have been built in Middle Asia and the Caucasus.

Linen weaving is also concentrated east of Moscow, although in separate towns from those devoted to cotton spinning. Production increased but slightly between 1913 and 1935.

Food industries gained fourfold from 1913 to 1935. Meat packing in the steppe follows the agricultural margin, with important centers at Saratov on the Volga, and in central Siberia at Kurgan, Petropavlovsk, Novosibirsk, Barnaul, and Semipalatinsk. Siberian butter was exported to England extensively before the First World War.

Sugar, refined from sugar beets, is a significant Ukrainian industry southwest of Kiev and northwest of Kharkov. The

Caucasus are noted for wine and canned fruits. Flour production conforms to the wheat areas, in the Ukraine and in western Siberia along the railway.

Fishing is most important around Astrakhan at the mouth of the Volga, where sturgeon and caviar are dominant. Rostov and the Sea of Azov occupy second place, followed by Murmansk, Vladivostok, and Kamchatka.

One of the few essentials not originally available in the U.S.S.R. was natural rubber. Although *Hevea braziliensis* cannot be grown, desert plants such as native kok-zaghiz or the Mexican guayule are cultivated from the Tien Shan west to White Russia. Artificial rubber is obtained from potatoes in factories at Yaroslavl and Kazan, from limestone at Erevan in Armenia, and from petroleum at Baku.

The expansion of industry under the five-year programs is shown in Vol. I of the Great Soviet World Atlas where significant maps compare the industry of 1913 with that of 1935 (Plates 147-152). Both in geographic extent and in quantity, the contrasts are enormous. Siberia developed notably, but manufacturing in the European areas expanded even more. The industrial production for 1935 is shown below:

Cities with production from 7 to 10,000 million rubles:
  Moscow—machine construction, textiles, food, chemicals.
  Leningrad—machine construction, chemicals, shoes and clothing, textiles.
Cities with production from 1 to 2,000 million rubles:
  Gorki—machine construction, food.
  Kharkov—machine construction, food, shoes, and clothing.
  Baku—oil, food, machine construction.
Cities with production from 500 to 1,000 million rubles:
  Odessa—machine construction, food, shoes, and clothing.
  Kiev—machine construction, food, shoes, and clothing.

Dniepropetrovsk—iron and steel, machine construction, chemicals, food.

Rostov-on-Don—machine construction, food, shoes, and clothing.

Stalingrad—machine construction, iron and steel, food, wood industries.

Yaroslavl—chemicals, machine construction, textiles, food.

Cities with production from 250 to 500 million rubles:

Tbilisi—food, machine construction, shoes and clothing, textiles.

Grozny—oil.

Mariupol—iron and steel, machine construction.

Taganrog—machine construction, iron and steel.

Stalino—iron and steel, food, machine construction.

Zaporozhe—iron and steel, machine construction.

Dnieprodzerzinsk—iron and steel, machine construction, chemicals.

Voronezh—machine construction, food, chemicals.

Tula—machine construction, iron and steel.

Kalinin—textiles, machine construction, shoes, and clothing.

Saratov—machine construction, food.

Kazan—shoes and clothing, food.

Ivanovo—textiles.

Magnitogorsk—iron and steel, ore, chemicals.

Chelyabinsk—machine construction, food.

Sverdlovsk—machine construction, food, iron and steel.

All cities with an industrial production in excess of 250 million rubles in 1935 lie in the European area. In Siberia there are 5 cities whose rank is between 100 and 250 million: Omsk, Novosibirsk, Stalinsk, Irkutsk, and Vladivostok; and one in Middle Asia: Tashkent. Cities of the same industrial output in the European area total 36. In the U.S.S.R. as a whole, 69 centers had an industrial output exceeding 100 million rubles in 1935. The corresponding total in 1913, with prices measured in 1926 to 1927 rubles, numbered but 5: Moscow, Leningrad, Baku, Ivanovo, and Odessa.

TRANSPORT

The transportation facilities of various areas differ widely. In the southwest there are closely spaced railways, while in the northeast, except for air transport, travel is restricted to widely spaced rivers or winter sled roads. Express trains on the Trans-Siberian cross the continent from the Polish frontier to Vladivostok in nine and a half days, or one may travel from Odessa on the Black Sea to Murmansk on the Arctic Ocean in three and a half days. But to traverse Siberia from Mongolia northward along the Yenisei requires more than two weeks by boat. Here again, continentality is inescapable.

Railways totaled 62,500 miles in 1940, as compared with 36,350 miles in 1913 excluding the areas lost during the First World War. This mileage, although but a quarter that of the United States, holds second place in the world. Freight turnover in the Soviet Union increased from 41 billion metric ton-miles in 1913 to 370 billion in 1939. In comparison, American railways carried over 750 billion standard ton-miles in 1944. In 1939, 1,626 locomotives and 49,100 railway cars were built. Soviet railways have a gauge of 5 feet in contrast to the standard gauge of 4 feet 8½ inches in western Europe and North America. Most freight cars have four axles as in the United States, rather than the two-axle type used in western Europe.

The distribution of railways, shown on the map of transportation facilities, strikingly corresponds to maps showing the location of cultivated land or population. The densest network is in the Donets Coal Basin, with the heaviest traffic moving between there and Kharkov. All the Union west of the Volga and south of Leningrad lies within 35 miles of a railway. The only other area with closely spaced lines is the central Urals. A coarse grid is developing south of the Trans-

Siberian. The Union's economic and cultural isolation is shown by the limited railway facilities across the borders. East of the Black Sea but five railways cross the long frontier: into Turkey, Iran, Mongolia, and two lines to Manchuria.

During the interwar period, extensive additions were made to this system, both in the older European area and in Asia. New railroads have been built and others double-tracked. In the west, one of the most important new lines connects Moscow and Rostov, via the Donets coal fields. When the Trans-Siberian was first built, it ran due east from Leningrad to Sverdlovsk and thence across Siberia. Passenger trains from Moscow are still routed north via Yaroslavl to this old route, but a new line has been built through Gorki and Kazan which provides a shorter route via Chelyabinsk.

Two spectacular railways lie north of the Trans-Siberian. The first runs to Vorkuta, near the northern Urals in the Pechora coal field, and possibly on to the Arctic. The second is the strategic Baikal-Amur project which leaves the old line at Taishet, between Krasnoyarsk and Irkutsk, runs north of Lake Baikal, crosses the upper Lena Valley, and will extend to the new city of Komsomolsk on the lower Amur, and continue to the Pacific opposite Sakhalin at the new harbor of Sovetskaya Gavan.

In Middle Asia, the first of the new lines was the Turk-Sib from near Tashkent to Semipalitinsk, linking Turkestan and Siberia. A newer line runs from Petropavlovsk south to Karaganda and Lake Balkhash. As the traffic of the Ural-Kuznets combine placed a great strain on the Trans-Siberian main line, a second railway has been constructed from Stalinsk westward to Magnitogorsk, passing near Karaganda.

There are nearly 1,169 miles of electrified railways, operating in the Kola Peninsula, around suburban Moscow and Leningrad, in the Urals and Caucasus, and within the Kuznets Basin.

The utilization of waterways preceded railway construction and has expanded but slowly in recent years. Operating waterways in 1939 totaled 56,170 miles. The freight carried in 1938 was about 23 billion metric ton-miles, about one-tenth that of the railways. In 1913 the ratio was nearer one to three. Timber in rafts or barges represents over half the total, and minerals and construction materials each represent an eighth. Grain and coal are also important commodities.

The Volga is the leading inland waterway, and its freight accounts for half the total. Its closest competitor is the combined Neva and Svir which link Lake Ladoga and Lake Onega with Leningrad. The Ob, Yenisei, and Lena together account for but one-fourteenth, a fraction that indicates the backward character and sparse population of their drainage areas.

The Volga's direction, depth, and economic hinterland make it the country's premier waterway. Baku oil and Donets coal move upstream, while wood floats down current. Unfortunately the Volga empties into the landlocked Caspian. There have long been plans to build a canal from Stalingrad to the Don, in order that barges and small seagoing steamers might link the Caspian with the Black Sea, but such a project involves considerable engineering difficulties. In the delta below Astrakhan are sand bars that make transshipment necessary. The headwaters of the Volga system are connected with Lake Ladoga through the Mariinsk Canal, completed in 1808 and frequently enlarged. Moscow lies on a small tributary of the Volga, formerly too shallow for navigation and inadequate for the municipal water supply. The Moscow-Volga Canal, completed in 1937, diverts water from the upper Volga past the city, thus increasing the water supply and making it possible for barges drawing 8½ feet to reach Moscow from the Caspian.

The Baltic-White Sea Canal links the Gulf of Finland with the White Sea via Lake Onega and is open to vessels of 1,250 tons.

Seagoing ships operate extensively in the Caspian and Black seas, and to a lesser extent in the Baltic, Arctic, and Far East. Freight services link Odessa and Vladivostok via Suez or Panama. This coast-to-coast distance of 13,264 miles via Suez or 14,177 via Panama is reduced to 6,835 miles via the Northern Sea Route from Murmansk to Vladivostok. The ton mileage of ocean-borne freight in 1938 was slightly larger than that carried on the rivers.

Highways have never received much attention. Out of a total distance of 840,000 miles in 1938, only 60,000 were surfaced with gravel or cobblestones, and but 2,400 were asphalted. Natural dirt roads predominate—in summer notoriously deep in mud or dust and in winter a series of frozen ruts. The scarcity of crushed rock limits foundation material to sand or river gravel and handicaps both highways and railroads over much of the country.

In the absence of railways important highways or post roads lead into Chinese Sinkiang from Fergana and from Alma-Ata. Tannu Tuva and Outer Mongolia are connected with Minusinsk. An automobile road extends from the Aldan gold fields south to the Trans-Siberian, and an important route links Nagaevo and Magadan on the Sea of Okhotsk with the Kolyma gold area.

There are automobile factories at Moscow, Gorki, and Yaroslavl, and motor-truck plants at Leningrad, Chelyabinsk, Kharkov, and Stalingrad. The production in 1939 amounted to 171,100 trucks and 25,700 passenger cars, a slight decrease from the preceding year. Most of the trucks are used in industry or collective farms, while passenger cars are limited to the largest cities. Almost no passenger cars have been available for private purchase; the output is absorbed by government and industry. Moscow streets have western-style traffic, but even on the busiest streets of large cities such as Kiev one may find but few cars. Intercity motor traffic scarcely exists.

Aviation is the most rapidly developing form of Soviet transportation. Scheduled routes covered 86,800 miles in 1944 and linked Moscow with all centers, even across Siberia. Airplanes carried 292,700 passengers in 1938.

AGRICULTURE

There are no adequate statistics of land utilization for the country as a whole. According to the best estimate for 1928,[1] arable land potentially available for crops amounted to 432,700,000 acres, or 8 per cent of the Union. If meadows, grassland, and permanent pasture are added, the entire agricultural area covered but 13 per cent of the total of 5,392,-000,000 acres.

In the area west of the Urals, agricultural land as a whole rises to 43 per cent and, excluding the north of Soviet Europe, the percentage becomes 65, which is even larger than in the settled parts of several western European countries. Little undeveloped good land is to be found south of Leningrad, where the remaining forest covers 17 per cent. In this area, the rural population ranges from 65 to over 259 per square mile, as against 25 to 65 in the Mississippi Valley. Soviet Asia has but 2 per cent under cultivation, or 6 per cent in any agricultural use.

Tundra covers 1,270,000 square miles, while the taiga forest north of latitude 60° N. accounts for 3,900,000 square miles. Neither area offers important agricultural possibilities on account of climate and soil. Desert and semidesert land

[1] TIMOSHENKO, VLADIMIR P., "Agricultural Russia and the Wheat Problem," Stanford: Stanford University Press (1932).

in the south occupies 1,000,000 square miles where cultivation seems out of the question. Notable developments have occurred in limited areas but are not capable of indefinite expansion. No less than 6 per cent of the entire Union is covered with marsh or bog.

Optimistic agriculturalists place the limit of feasible cultivation near the Arctic Circle, but there is little expectation that normal agriculture will ever displace the Siberian taiga. Inadequate rainfall is an obstacle in the arid south, and irrigation possibilities are limited.

Climate, natural vegetation, and soil all emphasize the significance of the agricultural wedge from Leningrad to the Black Sea and east to Lake Baikal, with outliers toward the Pacific. This triangle is far from regular, and there are other areas in the Caucasus and Soviet Middle Asia, but its general pattern is obvious. The most important part of the Soviet Union lies toward the Atlantic rather than the Pacific.

The gradual expansion of this agricultural triangle epitomizes the history of Russia over many centuries. Not only has colonization advanced eastward into Asia; at the same time it has pressed northward into the forest and southward into the steppe. The advancing agricultural triangle is thus in effect a wedge of settlement which has been driven into Asia and has simultaneously occupied more and more land on either side of the triangle.

The Soviet Union has two agricultural frontiers. Along the cold north is a fringe of settlement where short growing seasons limit crop yields and where frost often brings total failure. To the south is a frontier of drought where limited and erratic rainfall makes cultivation precarious.

During the period from 1913 to 1940, the sown area rose from 262,455,000 to 373,217,000 acres. This increase was obtained from virgin steppeland in Siberia where 17,297,000 acres were put under cultivation during the Second Five-year

Plan, by the irrigation of dry lands east of the Volga or in Middle Asia, through drainage of marshes in White Russia, and as a result of plowing pasture or forage land no longer needed because of mechanization.

It is doubtful whether there are large possibilities for future expansion of cropland except in the steppe. Despite the country's vast size, much of it must remain agriculturally unproductive. Increased harvests will follow higher crop yields and better utilization rather than added farm acreage. Prior to the Revolution, part of the land always lay idle under the three-crop system of rotating cultivation, pasture, and fallow.

The total of 373,217,000 acres under cultivation (1940) for 170,467,186 people (1939) gives an average of 2.2 acres per person. This compares with 2.8 acres in the United States, or 0.45 in China. The United States and the Union of Soviet Socialist Republics have nearly the same crop area, but the respective rural populations are 53,820,000 (1940) and 114,557,000 (1939).

Crop figures for 1938, when the total was 338,386,000 acres, show the following distribution, in thousands of acres: spring wheat, 66,538; winter rye, 52,337; oats, 44,187; spring barley, 21,033; potatoes, 18,199; winter wheat, 8,665; sunflower, 7,770; legumes, 6,224; vegetables, 3,261; corn, 2,480; other crops, 118,837.

Famines have long been the curse of Russia, largely owing to erratic rainfall. Drought and the effects of revolutionary communism in 1921-1922 caused the death of 5,250,000 people. Famine occurred again in 1932-1933 when inadequate rainfall combined with excessive government grain collections and peasant sabotage. Many districts experienced their lowest rainfall in 150 years in 1938, but agricultural organization had developed to the point where extreme distress was avoided.

Soviet agriculture is organized under either collectives or state-operated farms. The former provide for cooperative share ownership under the active control of the government. On state farms, workers are paid wages; on the collectives they receive a share of the harvest according to their work. Both of these are socialist devices to bring efficiency to farming, parallel to the changes in industry. Individually owned farms have disappeared. In 1938 there were 242,400 collective farms, with an average sown area of 1,198 acres, and 3,961 state farms with an average sown area of 6,651 acres. Many of the latter represent pioneering expansion into previously untilled land.

Mechanization has brought increased efficiency in farm practice. Modern tractors and harvesting combines are provided through Machine Tractor Stations on a service contract with the farm. In 1938, the country had a total of 483,500 tractors and 153,500 combines.

Wheat and rye are the dominant crops. All grains together covered 253,030,400 acres out of the 338,280,000 plowed acres in 1938, with wheat alone accounting for 102,546,500 acres. Yields were 16.3 bushels of winter wheat per acre and 13.2 for spring wheat. Winter rye averaged 15.5 bushels per acre, spring barley 16.6, oats 26.5, corn 16.0, and rice 16.6.

New varieties of wheat have steadily pushed the area of cultivation northward to the vicinity of Leningrad, Moscow, Yaroslavl, and Gorki. Grain crops are even grown near the Arctic Circle. Winter wheat predominates in the Ukraine, and spring wheat east of the Don and in Siberia where the autumn is dry and snowfall light.

Although the grain harvest has increased from 80,100,-000 metric tons in 1913 to 94,990,000 metric tons in 1938, higher domestic consumption has absorbed the increase. During the five years preceding the First World War, July, 1909, to July, 1914, Russian wheat exports averaged 165,-

000,000 bushels, in contrast to 52,000,000 bushels from 1931 to 1936.

Technical crops have received special attention. Cotton production increased three and a half fold between 1913 and 1938, rising to over 5,000,000 acres. Whereas formerly limited to Soviet Middle Asia and a small area in the Transcaucasus, cotton is now also grown near Astrakhan on the Volga, along the Kuban River, and in the southern Ukraine as far north as 48° N. In 1913 Russia imported 196,000 tons of raw cotton, as compared with a domestic production of 223,000 tons. By 1937 the local yield was 854,000 tons, while imports dropped to 22,000 tons. Flax has long been important in White Russia, as well as around Moscow and Leningrad. In 1938 the Soviet Union credited itself with 86 per cent of the world total. Sugar beets are grown in great quantity in the Ukraine, around Kursk, and more recently in the Caucasus, Middle Asia, and the Far East.

Subtropical crops such as grapes, tea, oranges, and other citrus fruit are increasing in the Transcaucasus. Thus Georgia produced 132,000,000 pounds of tea in 1943, and 430,000,000 oranges and lemons.

The U.S.S.R. appears to lead the world in the total production of rye, barley, oats, potatoes, flax, and sugar beets. Wheat production may also hold first place, with uncertainty due to the statistics for China.

FOREIGN INTERCOURSE

Between the First and Second World Wars the Union of Soviet Socialist Republics lived more nearly to itself than any other important nation. Few foreigners crossed its borders, and only a handful of Soviet citizens left on official business. Internal economy was entirely divorced from international finance. This fact, plus the pioneering economy of the five-year programs, enabled the Soviet Union largely to escape the world-wide depression of the 1930's. There was no other major country where one might go through the shops and find not a single article of foreign manufacture, or even a magazine or book from abroad.

Foreign trade is a government monopoly, limited to vital imports and the exports with which to pay for them. The fortunate abundance of domestic resources, plus frequent political obstacles to trade imposed by foreign nations, led the Soviets to develop an extreme nationalistic economy.

Imports during the interwar years consisted of complex machinery and tools, even complete factories, metals such as copper and aluminum, oil-well equipment and pipe, raw cotton, and rubber. Exports included timber, manganese, furs and bristles, anthracite, asbestos, and fertilizers, together with some oil and wheat. Political ends have been involved in the export of automobiles and trucks, cotton cloth, and textile and agricultural machinery to peripheral states such as Outer Mongolia, Tannu Tuva, Chinese Sinkiang, Iran, Afghanistan, Rumania, Bulgaria, and the Baltic States of Latvia, Lithuania, and Estonia.

Trade with the United States has shown wide fluctuations, and Soviet imports have always greatly exceeded sales. During the First World War, and again in the First Five-year Plan, imports exceeded $100,000,000. They then dropped to $9,000,000 in 1933 and rose steadily to $86,943,000 in 1940. Shipments from the United States in that year included machine tools, oil-well equipment, copper, molybdenum, and cotton, plus gasoline and wheat for the Far East. In return, the United States received manganese for its steel industry, anthracite consigned to New England, furs, and gold. American shipments during the years 1941 and 1942 totaled $3,000,000,000, largely under lend-lease agreements.

7

REGIONS OF SOVIET EUROPE

THE REGIONAL FRAMEWORK

THE Union of Soviet Socialist Republics is too large and diverse to be described by simple areal generalizations. Few geographic characteristics are everywhere present except as they are related to a unique political system and a common history. Climate and thus natural vegetation and soil differ strikingly from north to south. So too do land utilization and the mode of life. These larger differences of geography divide the Soviet Union into three major provinces: the old lands of Soviet Europe in the west, the dry province of Soviet Middle Asia to the south, and the vast pioneering expanse of Soviet Siberia in the east.

These provinces in turn may be divided into 24 regions, and the subdivision further broken down as much as desired. As the country is divided into successively smaller areas, generalizations become more valid. Thus one may describe the geography of Siberia more clearly than that of Eurasia as a whole, or White Russia with more detail than for all of Soviet Europe. Regions do not represent the end of subdivision, but they do have sufficient geographic unity and coherence to make them understandable.

Some of the regions are merely designated by their political place name, for these adequately define the geographic area. Topographic words such as plains or mountains are frequently employed. Some regions are typified by their natural vegetation or land use. Geographic regions are based on the total geographic landscape. Other lists in subsequent chapters deal with surface configuration, climate, or similar single elements, which taken together make up the totality of geography.

PROVINCES AND REGIONS OF THE SOVIET UNION

Soviet Europe	Soviet Middle Asia	Soviet Siberia
Ukrainia	Caucasia	West Siberian Agricul-
White Russia	Caspian Desert	tural Plain
Baltic States	Pamirs and Associated	Altai-Sayan Mountains
Metropolitan Leningrad	Ranges	Ob Taiga
Kola-Karelian Taiga	Oases of Southern Turan	Yenisei Taiga
Dvina-Pechora Taiga	Aral-Balkhash Desert	Arctic Fringe
Central Agricultural		Baikalia
Plain		Lena Taiga
Metropolitan Moscow		Northeastern Moun-
Southern Agricultural		tains
Plain		The Far East
Ural Mountains		

The face of the earth may be likened to a vast mosaic in which there is an infinite amount of detail. Each fragment of land has its own characteristics and bears little resemblance to the whole. Only as we view the ensemble as a unit does the microscopic detail disappear and the picture take on significance.

So it is with the Soviet earth. Each farm or hillside has its unique personality, of interest to those who live there but of little significance to the nation as a whole. Geography is interested in this micropattern chiefly as it reveals the characteristics of the larger region and makes generalizations valid. Integrated panoramas are more meaningful than the details of individual fields. Regional generalizations enable us to understand interrelationships, but they must be based upon an understanding of the individual components of the mosaic.

The function of geography is to clothe the map with significance, to give character and meaning to the face of the earth, and to differentiate the personality of one region from that of another. In the geographic landscape the totality of land and water and air and people is merged in their mutual interrelations.

Each geographic region is a unit. In some areas the dominant characteristic is climate, as for example with the desert; elsewhere regional coherence is provided by agriculture or by the drainage basin of a major river. Regional boundaries are seldom precise, but it is usually possible to block out landscapes each of which has a different personality from that of its neighbor. The map of geographic provinces and regions is drawn on a land-form base but the boundaries are cultural as well as physical.

If Europe starts at the Urals, half of it lies within the Union of Soviet Socialist Republics, but if "Asia begins with Russia," then the real boundary is along the west of the Soviet Union. Traditional Europe is the peninsular area of western Eurasia, with historic relations to the penetrating seas. In the continental portion to the east, Slavic peoples and undistinguished topography have long differentiated the landscape from that of Europe proper. More recently socialist ideology has given the Soviet frontier inescapable geographic meaning.

Environmental conditions in Soviet Europe are less favorable than in Germany or even Poland. Rainfall is lower and the variability greater. Farming has been primitive until recently, yet population increase has crowded the land as densely as in more prosperous countries. ". . . the Russians actually utilize their agricultural possibilities much more fully than do the people of the United States. If New England and northern New York, for example, were in Russia, their abandoned farms would undoubtedly be cultivated and would yield well above the Russian average." [1]

Soviet Europe may be divided into ten geographical re-

[1] VAN VALKENBURG, SAMUEL, and ELLSWORTH HUNTINGTON, "Europe," New York: Wiley (1935), 577.

Subtropical Mediterranean foliage typifies the health resorts of southern Crimea. This view is in Yalta. (*Sovfoto*)

The Crimean Riviera provides recreational facilities for many Soviet workers. (*Sovfoto*)

The plains of Ukrainia have some of the finest wheatlands in the world. A large part of Soviet agriculture is mechanized. (*Sovfoto*)

Odessa is the principal harbor of the Ukraine. (*Sovfoto*)

gions, each with its characteristic landscape. The following presentation starts with the Ukraine in the south and proceeds in a clockwise direction to Leningrad and the Arctic and thence south and east, ending with the Urals.

UKRAINIA

Political divisions seldom coincide with geographic regions, but this is nearly the case with the Ukraine. This geographic entity includes all of the Ukrainian Soviet Socialist Republic, the northern part of the Crimea, and the continuation of the Donets Coal Basin beyond the river of the same name. As here used, the Ukraine refers to the political area and Ukrainia to the larger geographic region.

Ukrainia has had a stormy history, marked by numerous invasions of Turks, Mongols, Poles, and Lithuanians, as well as Great Russians. The very word means "on the border." Kiev was the center of a Rus state in the eleventh and twelfth centuries and is still known as the Mother of Russia. German forces occupied the area at the close of the First World War, and Kiev was again an early objective in 1941.

Although comprising but one-fiftieth of the area of the entire Soviet Union, Ukrainia has one-fifth of the population and cultivated land, producing about one-quarter of the wheat and millet as well as two-thirds of the sugar beets. Of the Soviet totals, Ukrainia accounts for half of the coal, two-thirds of the iron, and one-third of the railway traffic. No other area is so fertile, so productive, or so densely populated. Despite the geographic spread of industry during the five-year plans, the Ukraine still retains a unique significance in Soviet economics.

The region has an essential cultural unity, but a basic occupational distinction can be drawn between green Ukrainia with its agriculture and black Ukrainia with its iron and steel. Farm lands may further be divided into the more moist northwest and the semiarid southeast, a division reflecting the transition from the scattered northern forests to the southern open steppe along the Black Sea.

Ukrainia covers nearly 200,000 square miles. If superimposed on the same latitudes in North America, it would bisect the United States–Canadian boundary. Conditions of climate and vegetation resemble the Great Plains of Montana and Saskatchewan. Through the center flows the navigable Dnieper, third longest river in Europe, while in the west are the Bug and Dniester and in the east the Donets and Don. These rivers wander across featureless country, in most places no more than a few hundred feet above sea level. Hills cross central Ukrainia from west to east, with elevations up to 1,200 feet. Buried crystalline rocks appear in the deeper valleys through this central area. Above them lie young sedimentaries, with a general east-west strike, which form low cuestas or escarpments along the middle courses of the several rivers. In the west, these cuestas are parts of the Volyno-Podolsk Plateau, a continuation of Carpathian foothills; in the east, the Donets Ridge exposes the deeply eroded roots of ancient mountains.

These structures are reflected in the course of the Dnieper, which at Kiev has a flood plain 10 to 12 miles wide on the left or northeast and a 300-foot bluff rising steeply on the right. After following this escarpment 250 miles to the southeast, the river abruptly cuts through the hills with a series of rapids, apparently in an antecedent course, and flows southwest to the sea, 170 miles distant. The Don and Donets have similar courses.

Winters are severe, for cold air masses sweep from the north without obstruction. Even the harbor of Odessa is frozen for several weeks each year. Kiev and Kharkov may experience temperatures of $-22°$ F. In spring and summer, desiccating winds from interior Asia bring dry air and may lift July temperatures as high as 130° F.

Annual precipitation varies from 22 to 24 inches north of the central hills to 14 and 18 inches in the Black Sea steppe. The hills are too low to account for this difference, which seems related to the Carpathian barrier rising to the west

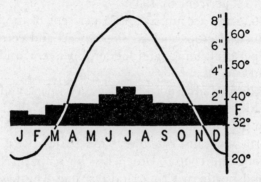

Kiev has a climate which is representative of the central Ukraine, with extremes of temperature in both summer and winter which are not represented by this graph of monthly averages. Elevation, 590 feet; average temperature, 44.2° F.; total precipitation, 21.1 inches.

across the path of Atlantic moisture. In farming, a constant effort is necessary to conserve the light winter snowfall and critical spring rain. These are as important as the summer rainfall.

Although the continental ice sheet covered only the middle valley of the Dnieper, its indirect effects are widespread. Much of Ukrainia is veneered with wind-laid loess, blown outward from the glaciated regions or derived from outwash flood plains. The resulting black chernozem soil is exceptionally high in organic material and lime and has maintained its fertility despite centuries of utilization. Chestnut-brown soils prevail in the driest areas to the south, and podsolic types occur in the limited forest section of the north.

Agriculture is important. In 1935, the Ukraine harvested crops on 63,534,500 acres. The area of the Republic is 171,-600 square miles, of which 87 per cent may be classed as potentially productive for cultivation, pasture, or forest. Forest land amounted to 12 per cent in 1891 but had dropped to 7 per cent by 1935.

In 1935, grain accounted for 75 per cent of the harvested area, industrial crops such as sugar beets and cotton represented 9 per cent, forage and fodder 8 per cent, and potatoes 5 per cent.

In the limited area north of Kiev, rye, oats, and potatoes are the chief crops. Winter wheat dominates all the central area from the Dniester to the Donets, supplemented by sugar beets, corn, soybeans, sunflower, and barley. Rice is locally raised along the central Dnieper. The semiarid Black Sea littoral and northern Crimea raise spring wheat, sunflower, rye, oats, and cotton.

Wheat output fluctuates widely with the climate and planned crop diversification. Thus the Ukraine yield in 1931 was reported as 237,000,000 bushels, in 1933 as 309,-000,000, and in 1934 as 145,000,000 bushels. Prior to the First World War there was a large surplus for export.

Technical crops include sugar beets, in which this region leads all others by far, sunflower, hemp, flax, 500,000 acres of cotton, and tobacco. Horses, cattle, and pigs are of only local importance.

Although Ukrainia was once termed the granary of Russia, expansion of agriculture elsewhere has decreased its proportionate place. Very little undeveloped farm land remains, and the map of land utilization shows the densest pattern of any part of the nation. Here as elsewhere, forced collectivization in the early thirties was met by wholesale slaughter of livestock. Only the rapid introduction of tractors prevented widespread land abandonment. Although the number of draft animals has subsequently increased, the great dependence upon power from gasoline makes agriculture vulnerable in time of war.

The industry of Ukrainia exceeds agriculture in importance. Coal, iron ore, manganese, salt, kaolin, fire clay, plus hydroelectric power, make this a significant area for heavy industry. Prior to the Second World War it occupied third place in Europe, preceded by the lower Rhine and British Midlands. Soviet industry has since become so nationwide that the proportionate rank of Ukrainia has declined.

The Donets coal fields occupy a structural basin that outcrops as a topographic ridge south of the Donets River. Within this area of 230 miles from east to west and 50 miles in width are a dozen important cities and some 200 mines. About an eighth of the production comes from east of the political limits of the Ukraine. Both anthracite and bituminous coals are mined, much of the latter making excellent coke.

Excellent iron ore is produced in the vicinity of Krivoi Rog, 200 miles west of the coal. Since most of the ore moves to the coal, the western part of the coal basin is most developed, with blast furnaces at Makeevka, Stalino, and elsewhere. Iron industries have also arisen near the ore, and at intermediate points where the connecting railways cross the Dnieper at Dniepropetrovsk and Zaporozhe. At the latter, electricity is used in the making of alloy steels. Manganese fortunately lies between coal and ore, and there is adequate fluxing limestone.

In addition to this east-west combine, ore and coal move north and south between the Donets and Kerch at the eastern end of Crimea. Kerch ore is not equal to that of Krivoi Rog, but there are important furnaces at Mariupol and Kerch.

These basic resources have given rise to a great variety of subsidiary industries, including cement, brick, chinaware, chemicals, aluminum, glass, and machine building. Those

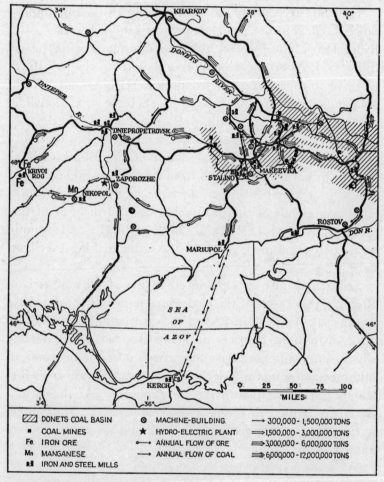

Southern Ukrainia is the major center of heavy industry, based on coal in the Donets basin, iron ore from Krivoi Rog, manganese from Nikopol, and hydroelectric power at Zaporozhe.

which require hydroelectric power are clustered about the dam near Zaporozhe; those which utilize coal are in the Donets area. Where skilled labor is vital and fabrication important, industries gravitate toward Kharkov.

Despite great destruction during the war, the Soviets reported that by the end of 1944 a considerable part of Ukrainian heavy industry was again in production. Thus in the Stalino district 7 blast furnaces, 23 open-hearth furnaces, 17 rolling mills, and 42 coke batteries were in operation. At Dniepropetrovsk 2 blast furnaces and 8 open-hearth furnaces were in service. In the Donets coal area 700 mines were again in operation.

The Ukraine is the most urbanized section of the Union. In 1939 the population of the Republic was 30,960,221, of whom 11,195,620 lived in 556 "city points." The population of this region appears to have approached a saturation point, since the estimate for 1931 was 29,042,000 and for 1933 was 31,902,000. Nine-tenths of the people are Ukrainians. Following the extension of the republic westward, the population amounted to about 38,900,000 in 1940.

Within the region are 17 cities with a population over 100,000. Kiev, the capital, is the largest with 846,293 people in 1939, placing it after Moscow and Leningrad. The city is beautifully situated on the right bank of the Dnieper near the junction of the Desna. The commercial importance of its site was recognized, as early as the eighth century when Greek and Norse traders met here along a major trade route from the Baltic to the Black Sea. Later on, Kiev became a great religious center. Trade in wheat and sugar, general market functions, and simple industries such as clothing have been supplemented by food and machine industries. Shipbuilding is an old occupation.

Kharkov is the fourth city of the Union, with a population of 833,432 in 1939. Since the Donets coal and steel area is but 125 miles southeast, Kharkov has developed important heavy industries, such as tractors and farm implements, locomotives, machine tools, and electric generators, as well as agricultural products and clothing. Whereas Kiev is old, Kharkov was founded in the seventeenth century. The city

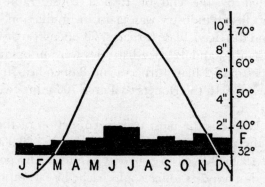

The climate of Odessa is characterized by low rainfall and three months with average temperatures below freezing. Elevation, 210 feet; average temperature, 49.3° F.; total precipitation, 16.1 inches.

lies 461 miles south of Moscow on the direct railway to the Crimea.

The third city of Ukrainia is Odessa, picturesque seaport on the Black Sea. The population was 604,223 in 1939. Odessa's foreign trade has fluctuated widely with the exportable surplus of wheat and with Soviet political developments. There are excellent harbor facilities and considerable coastal trade but surprisingly limited foreign service, for passenger facilities to Constantinople and the Mediterranean in 1936-1937 were limited to one Soviet boat every three weeks. This reflects the exceedingly meager ·contact between the Soviet Union and the outside world. The city increased less than 20 per cent from 1910 to 1935, while Kiev nearly doubled, and Kharkov even more. Industries include food products, agricultural machinery, and the evaporation of sea water for salt.

Rostov-on-Don, 510,253 in 1939, imports steel from the Donets area to the north and is a center of heavy industry much like Kharkov. Agricultural equipment is especially important. The near-by Sea of Azov yields large numbers of fish. Commerce in agricultural products includes leather and wheat from the surrounding steppes. This is the traditional center of the Don Cossacks.

The largest city within the Donets Basin is Stalino, 462,-395 in 1939. Near by is Makeevka with a population of 240,145. Each is a coal-mining town with great blast furnaces operating on Krivoi Rog ore. Just outside the basin on the north is Voroshilovgrad, formerly Lugansk, with 213,007 in 1939, the leading city for the manufacture of locomotives.

Three cities are grouped around the Dnieper rapids, submerged by the great dam from 1932 until its destruction in 1941. Here was the largest hydroelectric station in Europe, with a capacity of 900,000 kilowatts. The dam is 2,500 feet long and raises the water level 125 feet. To the north are Dniepropetrovsk, 500,662 in 1939, and Dnieprodzerzinsk, 147,829 in 1939. The new city of Zaporozhe, 289,188 in 1939, is at the dam itself. Abundant electric power and a position midway between Donets coal and Krivoi Rog iron ore have given these cities great industrial importance. All three have blast furnaces and important machine-building works. Zaporozhe has aluminum works and chemical plants.

Mariupol, 222,427 in 1939, and Taganrog are iron centers on the Sea of Azov. Taganrog also serves as a deepwater port for Rostov-on-Don. The ore center of Krivoi Rog, 197,621 in 1939, is the western outpost of steel production in Ukrainia. South of it lies the shipbuilding city of Nikolayev near the Black Sea.

At the beginning of the Second World War, the Soviet

Union reoccupied parts of eastern Poland ceded to the Union by the Treaty of Brest-Litovsk but lost during the civil war. That part of the area inhabited by Ukrainians was added to the Ukrainian Republic and may be regarded as a continuation of the geographic region here described. The area contains oil, gas, coal, iron, and zinc in modest amounts.

Wartime destruction in the Ukraine was so great, and evacuation, particularly of industrial equipment, so thorough, that restoration of economy to prewar levels will be a matter of years. Although the natural resources of the area make it certain that the type of economy will be similar to that existing before the war, there will probably be great changes in the size and relative importance of given cities. Important though it will be, the Ukraine may not again occupy the dominating place in certain fields of heavy industry that it held before the war. As a matter of fact, the war served to accelerate the planned shift of Soviet economy to the east. Although the U.S.S.R. will probably be in closer economic, cultural, and diplomatic contact with the Western World than ever before, it will, for the first time, have a really significant proportion of its population and economy in Asia.

WHITE RUSSIA

The Belorussian Soviet Socialist Republic, commonly known as White Russia, is a region of glacially formed swampland along the western border of the Union. Reacquisition of portions of Poland in 1940 extended the Republic westward and increased its original area of 80,000 square miles by more than a third. The population in 1939 before the expansion numbered 5,567,976, of whom 1,372,132 were classed as urban. There are 101 "city points," but only three exceeded 100,000 in size. The capital is Minsk, with 238,772 people in 1939. The 1940 population of the enlarged republic was about 10,300,000.

White Russia includes the hilly swampland at the headwaters of the south-flowing Dnieper and Pripet, and Baltic drainage in the basin of the Western Dvina. The following description refers primarily to the original area. A tenth of the region is a bog, much of it in the Pripet or Polesian marshes. In some areas the extensive lakes and channels make water transport more important than roadways. The Pripet and Bug rivers are connected by an important canal, providing barge service west to Germany. The small villages cluster on sand dunes or natural levees. Even in the more hilly lands to the north there are a great many undrained depressions in the glacial drift. The lakes and rivers are an important source of fish, but the country is too low for much water power.

The Baltic Sea makes the climate less continental than elsewhere. Rainfall is 22 to 24 inches, which is quite adequate since the evaporation is low. Drought is a rare hazard. Mixed forests of oak, linden, and maple with some spruce and fir cover a quarter of the surface. Hemlock and oak supply tanbark for an important leather industry.

Wet and acid soils limit agriculture to a sown area of 10,000,000 acres, of which 1,740,000 are recently drained swamps. Grain crops are chiefly rye and oats, but local output is below consumption and wheat is imported from the Ukraine. Root vegetables like beets, turnips, and potatoes do well. In the south hemp is grown, in the north flax, which is shipped to Moscow for processing. Pigs are important.

The lack of minerals restricts industry. Peat is used in homes and in central electric generating stations, with a production of 2,500,000 tons in 1937. Lumber, paper, leather, bristles, and meat are notable products. The surplus is shipped by waterway north to Riga on the Baltic or south to Kiev.

White Russia is one of the most backward regions of Soviet Europe. Rural areas have been retarded by unfavorable soils and a topography that makes transport difficult, while urban centers have developed slowly for want of a productive countryside and industry. Population distribution is very uneven; some areas have less than 2 people per square mile; others rise to 130. The people represent one of the purest groups of Slavs; many of them have lived here without mixture since they fled from the Tatar invasion in the thirteenth century. Polish influence is important toward the west.

Military operations overran the area during both the First and Second World Wars. In each instance the vast Pripet Marshes were of great strategic significance. When Napoleon was retreating from Moscow in November, 1812, many of his remaining troops were drowned when ice gave way on the Berezina River east of Minsk.

THE BALTIC STATES

The Baltic Republics of Estonia, Latvia, and Lithuania face westward toward the cultures of Scandinavia and at the same time look eastward economically to the Russian Soviet Federation of Socialist Republics. No other part of the Soviet Union has had such extensive contacts with the outside world. Although this Baltic fringe has certain unique characteristics, it is traditionally part of Greater Russia.

Each of the states is an ethnographic unit, marked by its uniformity of language, history, culture, and even nationality. These might furnish proper grounds for political independence were it not that their strategic position between the great continental area of the Soviet Union and an arm of the Atlantic Sea seems to entitle the larger nation access to the Baltic. Leningrad and the Arctic harbors are insufficient outlets to the high seas for the trade of such an enormous area as the U.S.S.R. At the same time the unique backgrounds of Estonia, Latvia, and Lithuania entitle them to special consideration from the Union. The Soviet Union has always shown interest in the cultures of its minorities, but political and economic interests are also involved in this case. The acquisition of these republics gives the Soviet Union an additional 1,100 miles of coast line.

Much of this area has had a stormy history with alternate periods of Danish, Swedish, German, Polish, and Russian control. Each nation has experienced periods of expansion as when Lithuania extended to the Black Sea in the fourteenth century. Estonia and Latvia were added to the Russian Empire in 1721 and Lithuania in 1795, and continued thereafter as integral parts of Russia until the First World War. During this period they were firmly linked with Russian economy and numerous railroads were built to the Baltic ports of Tallinn, Riga, Libau, and Memel. Despite czarist attempts to impose Russian customs, each area retained its distinctive language and culture.

Following the civil war that set up the Soviet Union, Estonia, Latvia, and Lithuania declared their independence and became separate democracies in 1918. This period of independence continued until 1940 when they voted, possibly under duress, to join the Soviet Union, each as a separate Soviet socialist republic.

Since the twelfth century large numbers of German merchants have migrated into these areas, and their descendants came to occupy an important place in the commercial life of the cities and were also landed gentry in the countryside. Shortly before the return of these republics to the Soviet Union an estimated 70,000 to 80,000 of this German population were evacuated to Germany, but their influence remains.

Contacts with western Europe have given these republics a higher level of material prosperity than prevails to the east. Thus the state of education and urban developments are transitional between the interior and the lands west and south of the Baltic Sea. In some ways Latvia appears to be more progressive than either Estonia or Lithuania. These Baltic peoples are Protestants and Roman Catholics, in contrast to the Great Russians who are or were Greek Orthodox.

The typical landscape is that left by the continental ice sheets. Adjoining the Gulf of Finland is a belt of eskers; to the south of them lie exceptionally well-developed drumlins, some of the best in the world. Undulating glacial ground moraine covers most of the remaining area, with innumerable lakes. Drainage is considerably better than in the marshlands of Belorussia to the south. Most of the area lies below 500 feet. Boundaries for the most part are cultural rather than physical.

Peat deposits occur in some of the lower areas and are being used increasingly as fuel. Estonia has oil shales, but except for some limestone and phosphate, there are few other mineral resources.

No other part of Soviet Europe is so exposed to marine influences or has such a low range between summer and winter temperatures. Polar air masses nevertheless invade the area during the winter months to bring continental extremes. The growing season varies from 120 to 180 days. Between 20 and 25 inches of rain falls annually of which a considerable part occurs as snow during the winter months. Sections near the sea are damp and cloudy, particularly in winter.

This is a long-settled land, and most of the good soil is utilized for crops of rye, oats, barley, wheat, and flax. Soils tend to be acid and podsolic so that crop yields are low. Dairying is widespread in each of the three republics, and stock breeding and poultry keeping are more profitable than grain growing in some sections. As climatic conditions improve southward, agriculture is least developed in Estonia and the arable land totals less than half that in Lithuania. Population densities in Lithuania thus average 44 per square mile as compared with 30 in Latvia and 25 in Estonia. The principal exports are timber and wood products, flax and linseed oil, and dairy products.

Most industries rest directly on agriculture, forestry, and quarrying. Twenty per cent of the region is covered by forests, and an efficient system of forest control and development ensures permanence of this resource. Industry has been of small importance, and considerably less than 25 per cent of the people live in towns. There is no other section of the Union, apart from the Ukraine, which is so well supplied with railroads or which has so high a standard of living.

The acquisition of the Baltic States not only gives the Soviet Union a better frontier in the west but makes available the port of Riga. The harbor is usually ice-blocked from 60 to 90 days during the winter but icebreakers keep it open during much of this period. Riga had a population of 393,211 people in 1939 and has important textile and metal industries.

METROPOLITAN LENINGRAD

When the ancient Varangians from Sweden came into Russia, they found the easiest water passage through the Gulf of Finland up the Neva River to Lake Ladoga, thence south through the Volkhov River to Lake Ilmen and on. The shores of the gulf were exposed to attack and did not offer a suitable site for a city. Instead they built their trading center at Novgorod at the outlet of Lake Ilmen. For several centuries this remained the dominant city in the north, and became a member of the Hanseatic League.

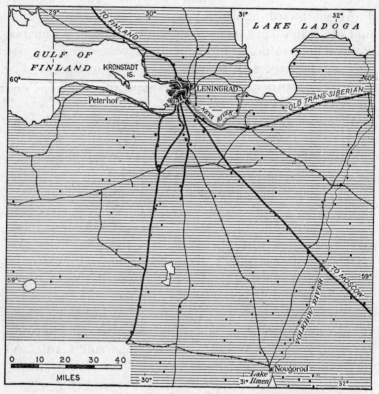

Leningrad lies at the mouth of the Neva River with access to Lake Ladoga and thence northward to the Baltic-White Sea Canal, and southward via the Volkhov River to Lake Ilmen and through the Mariinsk Canal to the Volga.

Sweden later recognized the importance of the Neva delta in continental trade and built forts there in 1300 and again in 1600. By defeating the Swedes in 1703, Peter the Great secured for Russia a "window to Europe," and in the same

Estonian women, in festival dress, are on parade in the city of Tallinn.
(*Sovfoto*)

The picturesque Latvian city of Riga lies on the Southern Dvina River,
near the Baltic. (*Sovfoto*)

St. Isaacs Cathedral is the finest church in Leningrad, completed in 1858 at a cost of 23,000,000 rubles. The dome is covered with gold. (*Sovfoto*)

Leningrad is a major export center for lumber. (*Sovfoto*)

year began construction of St. Petersburg, which was re-named Leningrad in 1924. Partly because the city actually has warmer winters than Moscow, Peter built his Winter Palace on the banks of the Neva. The site of the city was chosen because it provided access to the sea, and with little regard to its suitability for buildings. So many lives were lost in early construction that the city has the reputation of being built on bones. The surrounding delta has numerous distributaries and islands, so that the present city requires 500 bridges. Floods occasionally cause great damage, espe-cially when western winds pile up water in the gulf. During the winter, the Neva is frozen for six months, but icebreak-ers keep the harbor open except from mid-December to February.

Leningrad owes its importance to the larger setting rather than to its site. Waterways and short canals connect the Neva, via the surrounding Lakes Ladoga, Onega, and Ilmen, with the headwaters of the Volga, Dnieper, and Western Dvina. Lake Ladoga is the largest body of water in Europe and nearly the size of Lake Ontario; its southern margin is bordered by a canal to safeguard navigation. The Stalin Canal leads from Lake Onega north to the White Sea. These waterways make Leningrad the natural sea outlet for the trade of the Volga, the Ural and Caspian areas, and even western Siberia. These facilities became important as early as the eighteenth century, giving Leningrad a commercial and industrial advantage never surpassed by any other Rus-sian city. In earlier years Ural metals as well as Volga grain and livestock found their outlet here.

In exchange for these export shipments, Leningrad early received coal and machinery from England and Germany, cotton from the United States, jute from India, and rubber from the tropics. Foreign capital and engineering skill helped to make the city Russia's leading factory center, especially for technical work. Thus Leningrad acquired an accumulation of skilled and industrial facilities. Riga might provide a better entrepôt on the Baltic, but even with the substitution of rail transport for waterways, Leningrad's historic lead remains.

Industrial facilities in the Leningrad region prior to the war provided 75 per cent of the shipbuilding in the Union, 50 per cent of the electrical equipment, 35 per cent of the paper, 25 per cent of the machine building, 25 per cent of the chemical industry, and important contributions in the field of textiles, furs, shoes, typewriters, rayon, and furniture. Although the five-year programs were designed to spread industry across the Union, the products of Leningrad are so indispensable that production has grown over fivefold. Electrical power is obtained from two plants that use peat and from two hydroelectric stations, as well as from coal.

Shipping entering the port in 1933 amounted to but 2,-098,000 registered tons, which did not place Leningrad among the 50 leading ports of the world. Lumber was the major export, while machinery was imported. In 1936-1937, passenger service was limited to one Soviet steamer a week to London, plus an additional weekly sailing during the summer, and ten summer calls by the French Line. Rail transport has far surpassed water, with 11 lines radiating from the city. The first line was that to Moscow, built in 1851. The Red Star Express covers the 403 miles in ten hours.

Few cities in the world are laid out along such handsome lines as was St. Petersburg. Its founder and the succeeding czars built magnificent public buildings, palaces, and churches. As the capital of an empire, the city became the leading cultural center. The museums of the Hermitage and the Winter Palace still house one of the greatest art collections in the world.

The fortress island of Kronstadt lies 15 miles west of Leningrad and is the country's chief naval base. A 27-foot dredged channel leads to the port of Leningrad.

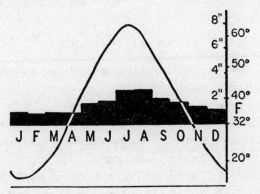

The climate of Leningrad reflects its maritime and continental position. Five months have average temperatures below freezing. Elevation, 30 feet; average temperature, 38.7° F.; total precipitation, 18.8 inches.

At the time of Peter's death in 1725, the population numbered 75,000. This increased to 192,000 by 1784, 861,000 in 1881, and 2,075,000 in 1913. After the Revolution, there was acute distress and the population fell to 722,000 in 1920, but in 1939 it reached 3,191,304.

The Leningrad geographic region approximately coincides with the oblast of the same name. Rainfall amounts to 24 inches, and agriculture is more handicapped by excess moisture and a high water table than by drought. January temperatures average 15° F., and the July average is 64° F. Snow falls as late as May. Half the region is covered with forest. Near Leningrad the cleared land is used for market gardens and dairy products; farther away are found potatoes, flax, and pigs. Rye is everywhere less important than hay and fodder crops.

Despite an unattractive site and political changes, Leningrad retains an industrial leadership because of its larger setting and inherited ability. It has well been said that Leningrad stands for skill, Moscow for strength, and Kiev for beauty.

KOLA-KARELIAN TAIGA

Karelia and the Kola Peninsula form the eastern margin of the Fenno-Scandian Shield. They resemble Finland, or central Canada, in their complex of ancient crystalline and metamorphic rocks, and in the effects of continental glaciation. Intense ice scour has stripped off the residual soil and smoothed the bedrock; elsewhere glacial debris covers the surface. Deep U-shaped valleys and coastal fiords reveal the intensity of ice action. Innumerable lakes, connected by swift rivers, cover over 10 per cent of the region. Most of the area is hilly and under 1,000 feet in elevation, with isolated mountains to 3,400 feet.

The region covers 105,000 square miles, about equally divided by the Kandalaksha embayment. From Leningrad to Murmansk is just 900 miles by rail, covered by the Polar Arrow Express in 38 hours.

Precipitation decreases from 24 inches in the south to 16 inches in the north. Most of the rain comes in the late summer. Snow falls from October through May, so that the frost-free period is under 100 days except in the south. Temperatures are lowest in the center away from the moderating influence of the ocean.

A taiga forest of pine, spruce, and birch covers 96 per cent of the land of Karelia and continues over much of the Kola Peninsula, bounded by tundra on the higher elevations and along the Arctic Coast. Most of the commercial timber is tributary to Leningrad, with Petrozavodsk as the chief mill town. Fish abound, especially cod and haddock from Arctic waters. The canning industry centers in Murmansk and Kandalaksha. The fur trade goes back to the early days of Novgorod.

Until the First World War, the region was sparsely inhabited except for a small Karelian population near Leningrad and reindeer-herding Lapps in the north.

In order to give Russia contact with the Allies during the First World War, the Murmansk Railway was hastily built in 1917. The section from Kandalaksha to Murmansk is now electrified. In 1933, the Stalin White Sea Canal linked the White Sea with Lake Onega and thus with the Baltic. The canal is closed by ice for six months and accommodates vessels only to 3,000 tons, but it has an importance somewhat comparable to the Kiel Canal in the case of Germany.

Since 1930 spectacular industrial developments have taken place north of the Arctic Circle. Near the railway and just east of Lake Imandra, is Khibin Mountain. This is an intrusion of nepheline syenite uniquely differentiated into 50 elements and many rare minerals. Apatite reserves total 2,000,-000,000 tons and are mined at a rate of 2,000,000 tons yearly for superphosphate fertilizer. Nepheline is even more abundant and provides a source of aluminum. These are the largest reserves in the world. Here the city of Kirovsk has grown from nothing to 50,000. Electric power is available near Kandalaksha, a few miles to the south.

Another isolated elevation is near Monchegorsk where nickel and copper reserves are second only to those at Norilsk on the Yenisei. Magnetite iron ore is near by.

Murmansk is the Soviet Union's gateway to the open Atlantic, and also the terminus of the Northern Sea Route to the Pacific. It is an important naval base and was a port for Allied supplies during the Second World War. The city lies 20 miles from the sea on the deep Kola fiord, where fresh water and the warmth of the Atlantic drift keep the harbor open the year around, the only ice-free port in the Union. From a population of some 3,000 in 1916, Murmansk grew to 117,054 in 1939. This is much the largest city anywhere within the Arctic Circle. To obtain fuel, the U.S.S.R. has a coal-mining concession in Spitzbergen which supplied 475,000 tons in 1936.

Agricultural conditions are unfavorable except in the extreme south near Petrozavodsk where hay and fodder crops support a small dairy industry. The great expansion of population in the north has brought a need for fresh vegetables, and experimental farms have made it possible to raise vegetables on several hundred acres around Kirovsk, and even at Murmansk.

DVINA-PECHORA TAIGA

The forest resources of the Soviet Union amount to 21 per cent of the world's timberland, although production is but 11 per cent. The area actually forested is 1,527,300,000 acres, of which 370,000,000 lie in Soviet Europe. Of this total forest area, 62 per cent is suitable for commercial exploitation. Pine and spruce account for nine-tenths of the conifers, with birch and aspen representing eight-tenths of the deciduous trees.

Forest products are the country's second largest export, normally ranking next to grain. Most of this goes to England, Germany, France, Holland, and Belgium. In normal years, Great Britain receives more timber from the Union than from all the rest of the world combined. In addition to sawn timber, there is a large trade in railroad ties, mine props, and pulpwood, but not in pulp or paper. As supplies diminish in Scandinavia, the reserves of northern Soviet Europe increase in importance. The increase in importance is also true of internal needs, since commercial forests in the Moscow area are nearly gone.

From Lake Ladoga to the Urals, and north of latitude 60° N., lies the country's finest coniferous forest, made up of Norway spruce, Scotch pine, larch, and fir, with scattered birch, alder, and willow. Tree growth is slow, for 18-inch logs are often 150 to 170 years old.

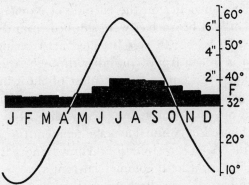

The port of Arkhangelsk has marked contrasts between summer and winter temperatures. Elevation, 50 feet; average temperature, 32.5° F.; total precipitation, 15.3 inches.

Since this forest roughly corresponds with Arctic drainage, it may be called the Dvina-Pechora Taiga, from the names of the two principal rivers. Other rivers of lesser importance are the Onega and the Mezen. Glacial debris and recent marine sediments mask the bedrock except in the low Timan Hills west of the Pechora.

Rivers are frozen from 180 to 200 days and are subject to serious spring floods before ice is cleared from their lower course in the north. During the summer they carry millions of logs, especially on the Dvina and its tributary the Vichegda.

Along the river banks, clearings extend two to six miles inland. The scattered population lives in drab log houses, raises hay for cattle, and grows a few vegetables such as cabbages and beets. Villages cling to the margin of a river or lake, or lie on the slopes of morainic hills away from the damp lowlands. In the south it is possible to raise fair crops of barley, rye, oats, flax, and hemp.

Arkhangelsk, or Archangel, is the leading city and the Union's largest mill center. The population numbered 281,-091 in 1939; yet it lies on the latitude of Nome, Alaska. In 1935, 8⅓ billion board feet were shipped from this port. In the preceding year, 546 vessels called at Arkhangelsk. The White Sea is frozen from November through April, but icebreakers keep the port open for most of the winter except when ice goes out of the rivers. The city lies 25 miles from the sea on one of the distributaries, with a 21-foot dredged channel. There is an annual average temperature of 32.5° F., with 15 inches of precipitation. Four hundred miles upstream is Kotlas, a local commercial center.

The timber of the Pechora Valley has scarcely been touched. Discoveries of oil at Ukhta and coal at Vorkuta are especially important because of the absence of mineral fuel elsewhere in the north.

CENTRAL AGRICULTURAL REGION

Environmental conditions divide the European portion of the Russian Soviet Federated Socialist Republics into three major zones. In the north is the relatively untouched Dvina-Pechora coniferous forest, in the center is the cleared mixed forest, and in the south is the cultivated steppe. Between the first two the boundary roughly follows the limits of Arctic drainage; between the second and third the boundary is determined by climate and vegetation. Whereas the center has over 20 inches of rainfall, the other regions receive less.

The Central Agricultural Region extends from the west-

The Red Square in Moscow is the focal point for Soviet festivals. The tomb of Lenin lies outside the Kremlin walls. Beyond is the picturesque cathedral of St. Basil. To the left are the old trading bazaars. (*Sovfoto*)

Within the Kremlin are a collection of palaces and churches which symbolize much of Russia's history. (*Sovfoto*)

The Lenin Library in Moscow holds the third largest collection of books in the world. This is the new building. (*Sovfoto*)

Heavy winter snows in Moscow are removed by modern American-style equipment. The building in the background is the New Moscow Hotel. (*Sovfoto*)

The Moscow subway is unquestionably the most ornate in the world. Each station is of different architectural design. (*Sovfoto*)

Streamlined excursion boats operate through the Moscow-Volga Canal. (*Sovfoto*)

Rebuilt Moscow has many modern buildings, such as this office for the newspaper Pravda. (*Sovfoto*)

ern frontier to the Urals. The northern limit lies near 60° N., just beyond the Trans-Siberian Railway from Leningrad to Molotov, formerly Perm, and the region continues south to an irregular line between 52 and 54° N., which bends south in the Kursk and Volga hills, and swings north in the Don and Volga lowlands. Except for industry in the larger cities, this region is dominantly agricultural, the home of millions of peasants who live very near the earth. Metropolitan Leningrad and Moscow are considered separately.

Almost the entire region is drained by the Volga and its tributaries, the Oka and Kama. This is the greatest river in Europe, with a length of 2,309 miles. It carries half the riverborne freight of the Union and is so important as a highway that it is nowhere bordered by a railroad.

Most of the region is an erosional plain, with gradients so gentle that floods do much damage. Except near the Urals the only elevations over 1,000 feet are in the Valdai, Smolensk-Moscow, and Pre-Volga Hills. Most of the region was glaciated, but strong morainic features are limited to the northwest quarter.

Of the 15 cities of over 100,000 population, 7 lie on the Volga. The westernmost of these is the textile center of Kalinin, at the crossing of the Moscow-Leningrad Railway. Farther downstream is the important city of Yaroslavl, the oldest Russian town on the Volga, and the point where the passenger trains of the Trans-Siberian line cross the river. Its industries include cotton and linen textiles, trucks, and rubber goods. The population was 298,065 in 1939.

Gorki, formerly Nizhni-Novgorod, is at the junction of the Oka. This is the metropolis of the upper Volga, long famous for its great fair which once brought as many as 400,000 visitors. It manufactures automobiles, paper, boats, and a large variety of metal goods and had 644,116 people in 1939. Kazan, noteworthy for leather, lies near the confluence of the Kazan and Volga rivers. The population was 401,665 in 1939.

The precipitation is about 20 inches, declining to the east. If rain falls at the proper seasons and the ground receives adequate moisture from melting snow, this is enough for normal agriculture; but unfortunately there are often serious variations. Most of the region has average annual temperatures between 35 and 40° F., with long and severe winters. The frost-free period is 120 to 150 days, exceptionally long for this latitude. The comparable period at the same latitude around Hudson's Bay is but 60 days.

This was a region of mixed conifers and deciduous forests. The largest remaining forest areas are east and north of Gorki, but even around Moscow trees cover two-fifths of the province. Houses are universally built of logs.

Prior to the Revolution, rye was the chief grain, for it is tolerant of podsol soils, cool summers, and the short growing season. The usual black bread is made of rye and molasses. Improvements in spring wheat have pushed its cultivation northward, and it now equals or exceeds the acreage of rye. Considerable land was added to cultivation from 1916 to 1935 through the clearing of forests and the draining of marshland.

Flax and sunflowers each occupy 6 per cent of the cropland. Potatoes and cabbages are widely grown. Livestock includes cattle, sheep, goats, horses, and pigs.

The industries reflect agriculture, for mineral resources are limited. Flour mills operate in many towns, and sugar, leather, felt boots, woolen cloth, and clothing are also important products. Lumber mills and woodworking industries cling to navigable rivers. Peasant handicrafts include lace at Vologda.

The people are largely Great Russians, but toward the east there are islands of Tatars, Bashkirs, and Chuvash, each in their own autonomous soviet socialist republic. Population densities range from 25 to 250 per square mile. In view of the inhospitable climate and poor soil, this represents a moderate crowding. Rural standards of living are low.

METROPOLITAN MOSCOW

Few cities in the world and none in the Soviet Union have the glamour that surrounds Moscow, more properly spelled Moskva. Its streets bring together picturesque Cossacks from the lower Volga, tribesmen from Uzbekistan, colorfully dressed visitors from the Transcaucasus, and nomads from the Arctic. Here is the seat of the Soviet government and the heart of Slavic culture. According to an old saying, "There is nothing above Moscow except the Kremlin, and nothing above the Kremlin except heaven." Urban rebuilding has liquidated many of the churches and other architectural monuments, but the Soviets cannot undo the history of the centuries even if they wished. The story of old Russia centers in the Red Square and the Kremlin.

Moscow was first mentioned in 1147 but was not important until after the decline of Kiev when Ivan III became the ruler of all Russia from 1462 to 1505. It remained the capital until Peter the Great removed the government to St. Petersburg in 1711, but several of his successors continued to favor the Kremlin as the proper capital of the country. Much of the city was destroyed in connection with Napoleon's invasion of 1812, but Moscow has always arisen greater from every conflagration.

In 1939, the population of Moscow numbered 4,137,018. This is a great increase from the 1912 figure of 1,617,000, and especially from the postrevolutionary low of 800,000 in 1920. The area in 1940 was 114 square miles.

The leadership of Moscow reflects its central geographic

position. Eleven railways focus on the city, four of them electrified in their suburban sections. Six of these lines are doubled tracked, two are three tracked, and one is a four-

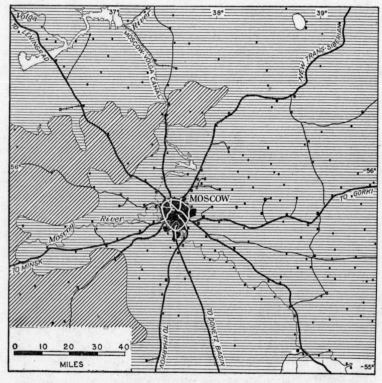

Eleven railway lines focus on Moscow. By virtue of the new Moscow-Volga Canal, the city now boasts of being "A Port of the Five Seas"; the White, Baltic, Caspian, Azov and Black.

track system. Long before railways, this was the center of trade routes which led northwest to Novgorod, north to Yaroslavl, east to Nizhni-Novgorod, now Gorki, south to the Ukraine, and even brought commerce from Siberia, Middle Asia, and Persia. The city lies in the broad plain of the upper Volga, Oka, and Don. Though Moscow is well to the west of the country as a whole, it is not far from the center of the triangle of population. As a result of the new 80-mile canal to the Volga, Moscow describes itself as the "Port of the Five Seas"—the Baltic, White, Caspian, Azov, and Black—but water-borne freight to such distances is lim-

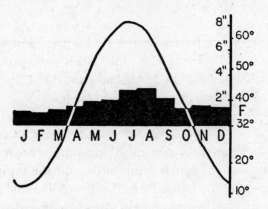

Moscow has climatic conditions which range from a January average of 12° F. and an extreme low of −44° F., to a July average of 66° F. and a maximum of 99° F. Elevation, 480 feet; average temperature, 39.0° F.; total precipitation, 21 inches.

ited. Modern automobile roads radiate to Leningrad, Minsk, Voronezh, Ryazan, Gorki, and Yaroslavl.

Climatic conditions are those of the Central Agricultural Region. With a latitude of 56° N., winter days are but six hours long and temperatures drop as low as −44° F., with a January mean of 14° F. Snow covers the ground for 150 days, to an average depth of a foot or two. Frost hazards require water mains to be laid 10 feet deep. During the long summer days the thermometer has reached 97° F., and there is a July average of 66° F.

The city lies on the shallow Moskva River, which flows in a series of broad meanders with undercut bluffs on the outer loops and sand bars on the inside of the bends. The earliest settlement was opposite a narrow island on a 130-foot bluff, where the Kremlin, which in Russian means citadel, was built, originally of wood. The present imposing brick parapets and towers date from Ivan III. This nucleus around which Moscow grew is now a collection of palaces, golden-domed churches, and government offices. In early days the Kremlin was the residence of the aristocracy. Outside its eastern gate was a bazaar on the Red Square and beyond it the homes of merchants. To protect this extramural area a second wall was built in 1534, known as the Chinese Wall although it had no connection with Tatars.

As Moscow grew, it expanded farther and a third and fourth wall were built, the latter within a radius of a mile and a half from the Kremlin. These outer two walls have been replaced by circular boulevards, and the built-up city today extends far beyond the limits of the old original nucleus. Streets have a cobweb pattern with radial arteries leading out through old gateways onto intercity highways. Cross streets are more or less concentric with the series of old city walls.

Old Moscow was a city of great contrasts. Most of it was a gigantic village of two-story houses. Magnificent streets with ornate structures alternated with irregular alleys and miserable hovels. The city lacked the metropolitan smart-ness of Paris or Berlin, and municipal services such as sani-tation were of limited development. In 1935, plans were drawn up for ten years of reconstruction, involving magnifi-cent subways, a great extension of housing and office build-ings, a new water supply, a notable widening of streets, and sweeping revisions in land use. Expenditures in the first five years amounted to ten billion rubles. No city has ever been so extensively rebuilt in modern times. Many parts have been altered beyond recognition. Housing needs are still urgent, for population continues to grow.

In 1940, there were 135,900 telephones, 27,592 hospital beds, and the daily water consumption was 59.7 gallons per capita. Eighty-two colleges had 94,987 students. There were 40 legitimate theaters and 55 moving-picture theaters. The Soviets have continued Russia's high tradition in the ballet, opera, and drama.

As an industrial area, prewar Moscow produced one-seventh of the manufactured goods of the nation. Consumer goods were once dominant, but heavy industry has become very significant. In 1940, the incoming freight of coal, oil, metals, lumber, grain, and raw cotton amounted to 22,900,-000 metric tons. Outgoing shipments were only 4,300,000 tons, made up of machinery and other metal products, prepared foodstuffs, textile, and clothing. The industrial area circles the residential city and includes factories for automobiles, agricultural machinery, flour, leather goods, cotton, flax, wool, electrical equipment, and machine tools. Large thermal-electric stations burn near-by lignite or peat and supply both electricity and steam for heating.

SOUTHERN AGRICULTURAL REGION

In terms of soil the agricultural possibilities of this region are among the most attractive in the entire Union; if judged by climate, the story is very different. Before the arrival of man this was a steppe, treeless except along the streams or in the moister north. For centuries it was the home of no-madic horsemen, the Cossacks of the lower Volga, Don, and Kuban rivers. Into these grasslands came Mongol warriors, and more recently the Russian farmer.

The yearly precipitation decreases from 20 inches in the west to as little as 12 inches in the southeast, with 16 inches a representative figure. Russian agronomists place the agricultural frontier at the 12-inch line, in contrast to American limits of 20 inches. Since low rainfall is associated with high variability, crop failures have been recurrent. In 1892 and 1921, drought reached the proportions of a national calamity.

This is the area of rich black chernozem and almost equally valuable chestnut-brown soils. Both are high in organic matter and soluble minerals, but their very richness is caused by insufficient water to leach the soil.

Successful agriculture depends on building up the soil moisture through careful conservation of winter snow and frequent cultivation to check evaporation. Shelter-belt planting has been used with moderate success for decades. Present irrigation developments are limited to the flood plains of the rivers, but two dams on the Volga near Kuibyshev will supply power to pump water into canals on the eastern Volga steppe.

Some of the largest state farms lie on the drier margins of agriculture in this region. Crop hazards are too uncertain to be risked by the individual, but by specialized techniques the government hopes to obtain a fair harvest in most years. In two decades prior to the First World War, there were three years of complete crop failure at Saratov on the Volga and but five good crops. Drought brings a risk to livestock as well as to grain. Under socialized planning it is thought that the government may move out the population and employ them elsewhere in drier years.

Spring wheat and winter rye are the dominant grains, followed by oats, barley, and millet. The only other crop of importance is sunflower, raised for its oil. Pre-1913 crops of spring wheat averaged but six to seven bushels per acre on the Volga.

Stalingrad is a major industrial center, with a 1939 population of 445,476. It receives coal and steel from the Donets

Basin, oil from Baku, and timber down the Volga. For 30 miles, industries line the Volga and include metallurgical works, tractors, shipbuilding, agricultural machinery, oil refining, and lumber yards. Stalingrad's importance will be further increased if a proposed 60-mile canal should link the Don and the Volga. The latter river is frozen 148 days. Although seriously damaged at the height of the German invasion, Stalingrad's location is so important that it is being rebuilt.

Kuibyshev, once known as Samara, is near the northern limit of the steppe. It lies on an eastward bend of the Volga and is a local commercial center. Huge hydroelectric projects will irrigate thousands of acres on the trans-Volga steppe. Near-by oil fields form a "Second Baku." The city numbered 390,267 in 1939. Kuibyshev became the temporary capital when Moscow was threatened during the Second World War.

Saratov on the Volga, midway between these preceding cities, had a population of 375,860 in 1939. Other cities include Voronezh on the Don, 326,836 in 1939.

THE URAL MOUNTAINS

The mineral wealth of the Urals has been known since the fifteenth century. The earliest developments yielded salt, silver, and gold; under Peter the Great, iron was smelted with the use of charcoal. By the nineteenth century, the region was also famous for its gems, semiprecious stones, gold, and platinum.

Developments under the five-year plans have been even more spectacular here than elsewhere. Great metallurgical plants have provided the base for heavy industry. Mining now includes coal, oil, iron, copper, gold, platinum, silver, nickel, aluminum, manganese, asbestos, lead, zinc, magnesium, chromium, potash, salt, and ornamental building stones. No part of the Soviet Union is so richly mineralized. Agriculture is of less importance but provides the materials for flour mills and leather tanning. The Urals are now the country's second industrial base, well removed from any frontier. But for their development, the Union might not have been able to carry on in the war against Germany.

Within the Ural region are eight industrial cities which had in excess of 100,000 people in 1939. Sverdlovsk, formerly Ekaterinburg, with 425,544 people, and Chelyabinsk, 273,127 people, are key centers for mining and manufacturing on the eastern side of the mountains. The former has a copper smelter, new blast furnaces, and very large works for heavy machines, while the latter mines lignite and manufactures tractors. Molotov, formerly Perm, 255,196, and Ufa, 245,863, are old cities in the western hills, less affected by mining. Nizhni Tagil and Magnitogorsk are giant steel centers in the central mountains, with important railway car shops at the former. The latter grew from nothing in 1929 to 145,870 in 1939.

Railways cross the central Urals at Nizhni Tagil, Sverdlovsk, and Chelyabinsk, and the south Urals at Orsk and Aktiubinsk, with another line west of Magnitogorsk. North-south lines parallel the mountains on either side. Several railroads are electrified.

The Urals are an old range, worn down to rounded hills. In the north the structure continues to the islands of Nova Zemlya, not included in this geographical region; in the south the Mogudjar Hills extend to the Aral Sea. As here considered, the Urals have an extent of 1,500 miles, with a maximum width of 325 miles in the latitude of Sverdlovsk.

On either side of the central crystalline and metamorphic core are geosynclines of upper Paleozoic sedimentaries. Extensive folding and thrusting from the east have complicated

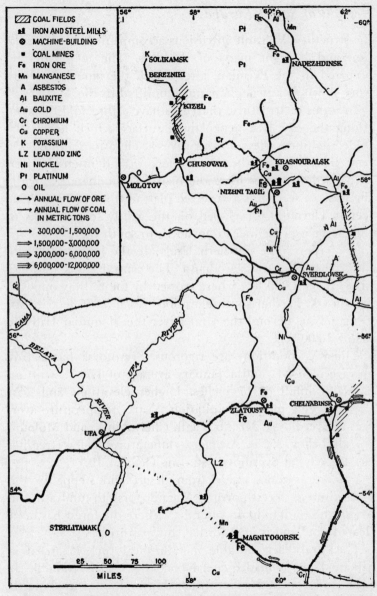

The Ural Mountains provide iron and a wide variety of industrial raw materials. This area carried the major burden of military production during World War II.

the structure. Volcanic intrusions accompanied the deformation and brought many of the ores. The major folding occurred in the Permian, after which the mountains were worn down to a peneplain and reuplifted in the Tertiary.

In terms of structure, the Urals have a threefold division. Along the east is a peneplained surface which bevels the folded sedimentaries and intrusives at elevations around 750 feet; in the center the crystalline core and intensely overthrust sedimentaries form the main mountain range; while the western section is a dissected plateau from 1,000 to 2,000 feet in elevation, developed on the gently folded rocks of the larger geosyncline. From north to south there is a fourfold division. The northern Urals are the highest and rise to 6,202 feet in Mt. Narodnaya. The central Urals are mere hills, under 1,000 feet where crossed by the railway opposite Sverdlovsk. Farther south elevations reach 5,376 feet in Mt. Yoman-Tau. Beyond the Ural River the Mogudjar Hills lie below 1,800 feet.

Climatic conditions are rigorous. Sverdlovsk has a July average of 63° F. and a January average of 1.7° F., with an annual rainfall of 17 inches. Higher elevations and west slopes receive more precipitation. Yearly temperature averages at Sverdlovsk, Nizhni Tagil, Chelyabinsk, and Molotov are all below 35° F. Average temperatures below freezing last 171 days at Sverdlovsk, starting October 19.

Vegetation zones grade from desert and steppe in the south through forest north of Magnitogorsk to tundra in the Arctic and on mountain summits. Where the forest has been cleared, the land is used for hay and pasture.

The Urals lack suitable metallurgical fuel. Charcoal is still used but is inadequate. Noncoking coal is available at Kizel and brown coal at Chelyabinsk. Prewar coal needs amounted to 20 million tons, of which half was brought from Kuznets or Karaganda in central Siberia. Oil is produced around Sterlitamak in the west. There are few hydroelectric developments.

Iron ore is the prime resource, with large deposits of magnetite near Nizhni Tagil, Zlatoust, and Magnitogorsk. Blast furnaces of very large dimensions operate at the first and last cities, and at Sverdlovsk. Some of the old charcoal plants

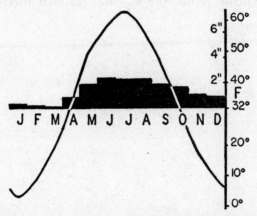

The climate extremes of Sverdlovsk reflect its remoteness from the moderating influences of the ocean. Average annual rainfall, 17 inches.

are still in production in the western hills. Manganese is present but is too high in phosphorus for satisfactory use. Iron production in the Urals amounted to 2,600,000 tons in 1937.

The problem of the metal industries here as elsewhere is that many exploited deposits are of inferior quality or are remotely located with respect to fuel or markets. For example, Magnitogorsk ore now appears less rich in iron and higher in sulphur than anticipated. Elsewhere the ore is titaniferous. The country urgently needs copper and, although the Urals have large smelters, the ore is unsatisfactory. The same is true of aluminum. Overambitious and overlarge plants, a product of the megalomania expressed in much early planning, have involved management difficulties. The significant fact is that despite all difficulties, socialist enthusiasm has achieved a noteworthy production; whether some ores are of too low grade to justify exploitation is a question that remains to be answered in a closed economy. In nationalistic terms, the war has justified their development.

8

REGIONS OF SOVIET MIDDLE ASIA

SOVIET Middle Asia is the driest and at the same time the most picturesque of the three Soviet geographic provinces. Nowhere else are there such beautiful snow-capped mountains or such colorful cultures.

The southern regions of the Soviet Union on either side of the Caspian are areas of young mountains and deserts, so distinct in climate and way of life that they deserve separate treatment. Since most of the area lies northwest of the Pamirs, the name Middle Asia is somewhat of a misnomer, but follows Russian usage. The Caucasus are often grouped with the "continent" of Europe, but this is merely a reflection of current political boundaries. Prior to the Russian conquests of the nineteenth century, this part of Eurasia, with long-standing Oriental contacts, belonged to Persia. Still earlier, Tamerlane ruled both Samarkand and Tbilisi, or Tiflis.

CAUCASIA

Caucasia is a world in itself. The region between the Black and Caspian seas comprises the alpine mountains and valleys from the Turkish frontier to the Kuban-Manych Plain. The mountains are geologically young but their human history is old, whereas with the Urals the reverse is true. Serving both as a bridge and a barrier to migration, this region has a long and dramatic history. Across its passes are major trade routes known to Assyrians and Romans. In the mountains, cultures have been cradled and found their grave.

Some thirty nationalities live in the region, many of them with picturesque native dress and colorful arts. These include Azerbaidzhanians, Georgians, Armenians, Russians, Ossetians, Abkhazians, Ajarians, Greeks, Kurds, and Jews. Bitter animosities have been the rule. This is the home of Joseph Stalin, a Georgian.

Three union republics lie south of the main range, but the geographic region also includes the north slopes within the Russian Soviet Federated Socialist Republics. From west to east these are the Georgian Soviet Socialist Republic, the Armenian S.S.R., and the Azerbaidzhanian S.S.R. The entire area comprises about 80,000 square miles, only 1 per cent of the Union, while the population is nearly 10 million, or some 5 per cent.

Caucasia includes three mountain ranges. The Greater Caucasus extends from the Caspian near Baku 685 miles northwest to the Black Sea beyond Novorossisk, and the same structures reappear in Crimea. In the south the Lesser Caucasus Range includes part of the high Armenian Plateau, largely in Turkey. Connecting these chains in the center are the low Suram Mountains. Between the main ranges are valleys that drain to the Black and Caspian seas. In the west is the Rion Valley and Colchis lowland, while the Kura River drains the eastern Iberian lowland.

In the Greater Caucasus folded Paleozoic formations occur in the center, together with extensive igneous rocks toward the west, but the flanks are made up of Jurassic and Tertiary beds. Folding occurred in the Cenozoic and was accompanied by extensive igneous activity. The highest mountain is volcanic Mt. Elbrus, 18,468 feet, which exceeds anything in Europe. Considerable areas are above the snow line, and there are 1,400 glaciers. The topography is superbly rugged. Serious earthquakes occur several times a century.

The connecting Suram Range is a granite massif which

The inner courtyard of a caravansary in Daghestan, near the Caucasus, provides space for both travelers and their animals. (*Sovfoto*)

Isolated settlements characterize the rugged topography of the Caucasian Highlands. (*Sovfoto*)

The Georgian Military Highway is the principal road across the central Caucasus. (*Sovfoto*)

Rich meadows provide summer pasture on the slopes of the northern Caucasus. These goats are in the Kabardino Balkarian A.S.S.R. (*Sovfoto*)

Baku is the fifth largest city in the Union. Here is a new moving-picture theater. (*Sovfoto*)

Cultural contrasts abound in Caucasia. This is a tea house in a Daghestan village northwest of Baku. (*Sovfoto*)

Houses of sun-dried bricks or pounded earth characterize the dry lands of the lower Volga. This is a Kalmuk home. (*Sovfoto*)

Large quantities of salt are secured from Baskounchak Lake, near the mouth of the Volga. (*Sovfoto*)

forms the watershed between the Rion and Kura rivers. There are passes as low as 3,280 feet.

The Lesser Caucasus is a block-faulted highland with numerous dormant volcanoes, generally from 6,000 to 10,000 feet. Lake Sevan lies in the center. Just across the border in Turkey is volcanic Mt. Ararat, 16,916 feet.

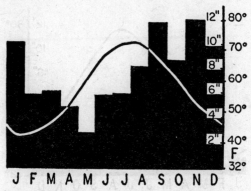

Batumi has a Mediterranean type of rainfall with a winter maximum and the highest precipitation of any city in the Union. Elevation, 20 feet; average temperature, 57.7° F.; total precipitation, 93.3 inches.

Climate and vegetation vary abruptly with altitude and exposure. The Black Sea littoral has Mediterranean subtropical conditions with 93 inches of rainfall at Batumi. The arid Caspian shore at Baku receives but 9 inches and has an annual temperature of 57° F. with mild winters and hot summers. The Greater Caucasus stops cold northerly winds, while the Suram Range blocks moisture from the west. Snow-capped mountains are seen through palm trees, while deserts and swamps are not far apart. The interior lowlands are similar to the northern Balkans, and along the Black Sea conditions resemble the French Riviera, whereas mountain climates duplicate Nova Zemlya. Deciduous forests cover the lower slopes, followed by conifers and meadows. The flora is exceptionally rich, including 6,000 varieties of flowers. Seifriz has remarked that "plants, like people, seemed to have stopped here in their migratory journeys."

Agriculture is noted for the variety of subtropical products. Corn is an old crop, but the area of cotton, grapes,

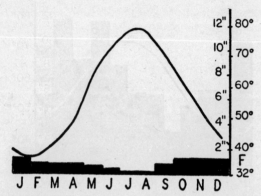

The climatic graph for Baku illustrates the aridity and high temperatures of the Caspian Desert. The average annual temperature is similar to that of Batumi, but the seasonal range is greater. Elevation, 0 feet; average temperature, 57.9° F.; total precipitation, 9.5 inches.

tobacco, and fruits has been greatly extended, and new crops added such as tea, citrus fruits, tung oil, cork oak, bamboo, and flax. The cultivated area has been expanded by draining swamplands in the Colchis lowland and by irrigation in the Iberian lowland. Wool and hides are produced in the highlands. In western Georgia, the area under tea increased from 2,400 acres in 1917 to 111,640 in 1937, with a production of nearly 5,000,000 pounds. In the same period orange and lemon groves rose from 395 to 25,000 acres. Occasional frosts are a hazard. Caucasian wines have long been famous.

Petroleum has been produced on the Apsheron Peninsula

at Baku since 1863. In 1901, Baku supplied half the world output and still accounts for 70 per cent of the Soviet production. There are two pipe lines to Batumi, but most of the oil is shipped by Caspian tankers to the Volga, so that Baku is the first seaport of the entire U.S.S.R. Considerable oil is also produced along the northern foot of the Caucasus near Grozny and Maikop.

Manganese deposits at Chiatury are exceptionally rich, with a production of 1,650,000 metric tons in 1937. Ore is shipped from Poti on the Black Sea to western Europe and the United States.

There are coal mines at Tkvarcheli and Tkvibuli. Hydroelectric possibilities are extensive, especially on the outlet from Lake Sevan. Small developments include copper, molybdenum, arsenic, and tungsten. Salt is obtained from the Caspian. Mineral waters are bottled along the northern foothills.

Three cities exceeded 100,000 in 1939, each the capital of its republic. Baku dominates Azerbaidzhan, with a 1939 population of 809,347, fifth city of the Union. Oil refining is the chief industry. Tbilisi, formerly spelled Tiflis, lies in the center of Transcaucasia on the upper Kura River, and is the capital of the Georgian S.S.R. Its population in 1939 was 519,175. The city was founded fifteen centuries ago and has numerous light industries. Erevan is the capital of Armenia, with 200,031 people in 1939. On the north slope of the Caucasus are Grozny, Ordzhonikidze, Kislovodsk, and Maikop.

Railways parallel the Greater Caucasus on the north and south. There is a line to Baku along the Caspian, and a Black Sea line was completed to Batumi in 1942. From Tbilisi another railway leads south into Armenia, but only automobile routes lead northward through the main range. The spectacular Georgian Military Highway, 130 miles long, was officially opened in 1814. The Ossetian Road is also passable for cars.

Southern Crimea is a detached portion of Caucasia, geologically similar, although its culture is more closely linked with the Ukraine. In the south the mountains descend abruptly to the Black Sea and protect the coast from cold northern winds. Although at latitude 45° N., the shore is a winter resort of some fame. Charming villas surround the city of Yalta.

CASPIAN DESERT

The Caspian Sea occupies the lowest part of a vast area where no runoff reaches the ocean. Were rainfall more abundant or evaporation less, the basin would be filled to overflowing. During the more humid glacial period, the enlarged Caspian drained westward to the Black Sea with an outlet at an elevation of 150 feet, whereas the surface is now 85 feet below sea level.

Seventy per cent of the water intake of the Caspian comes from the Volga and 19 per cent from direct precipitation. All of this is lost by evaporation. As conditions vary, the level of the sea fluctuates. In 1306 the surface was 44 feet higher than at present, while in 1845 it was 2 feet lower. Proposed diversions of Volga water near Kuibyshev will further lower the level. To balance this loss, it is possible that part of the Amu Darya may be diverted through an ancient bed from near the Aral Sea to the Caspian.

Attempts to correlate the fluctuating levels of the Caspian and Aral seas with climatic changes and the rise and fall of ancient civilizations are confusing. The Caspian level rises with cool wet summers along the Volga, whereas the Aral Sea level depends on melting snow in the Pamirs, with the most runoff during hot dry summers.

Surrounding the Caspian Sea is a desert of limited usability. Much of it is covered with Quaternary sand and clay laid down by the expanded sea and reworked by the wind.

Since the Caspian Desert is invaded during the winter by cold air masses, temperatures drop to −22° F. in the Volga delta and the river is frozen for 112 days. During the summer, dry winds heated to 104° F. come from the east and blow with high velocity.

Rainfall is from 4 to 12 inches, as compared with annual evaporation from a free-water surface amounting to 48 to 60 inches and from irrigated soil of 34 inches. Even the Volga and Ural diminish in size as they flow southward while in the winter the water of the Emba entirely evaporates before reaching the sea.

Agriculture is limited to strips of irrigation along the rivers. A few wandering nomads, Mongols or Kalmuks, raise sheep and camels. Fishing is very important in the northern Caspian, especially for sturgeon and caviar.

Three minerals are of importance. Oil is produced from salt domes along the Emba River under conditions resembling the Texas and Louisiana Gulf Coast. A pipe line runs 526 miles from Gurev on the coast through the Emba fields to Orsk in the southern Urals, with a possible extension east to Omsk.

Borax and other minerals are secured from rich deposits at Inder Lake, where the production of borax compounds amounts to 30,000 tons and places the U.S.S.R. second to the United States in world output.

At the eastern side of the Caspian is Kara-Bogaz Gulf, enclosed except for a shallow entrance 400 feet wide. This bay receives no rivers, and evaporation is so great that the water contains 29 per cent of salts. Mirabilite, or sodium sulphate, is precipitated naturally and other chemicals are extracted.

The principal city of the region is Astrakhan, on a distributary of the Volga. The population in 1939 numbered

253,655. The city has fish canneries and woodworking industries based on timber rafted down the Volga. Oil is the major import, but extensive sand bars make it necessary for Caspian tankers to unload into barges from which oil is transferred to river steamers at Astrakhan. Extensive dredging is proposed.

PAMIRS AND ASSOCIATED RANGES

Soviet frontiers reach into the Pamirs and the great ranges that radiate from the roof of the world. Within the region are the Union's two highest peaks, appropriately named Mt. Stalin, 24,584 feet, and Mt. Lenin, 22,377 feet. The second was originally thought to be the higher, and its name was changed from Kaufmann to Lenin, but corrected elevations showed the former Mt. Garbo to be of greater height and it was then renamed Mt. Stalin. The mountains form a continuous rampart between the Amu Darya and the Dzungarian Gate, a distance of 1,000 miles, and also include an outlier near the Caspian.

The structure of the numerous ranges is involved. The Pamirs are a mountainous plateau, mostly over 12,000 feet, with broad valleys five to ten miles wide cut by deep canyons and surrounded by rocky mountains. They lie between the Amu Darya and the Syr Darya.

The Tien Shan, or heavenly mountains, so named from their extension into China, lie north of the Pamirs. Within the Soviet Union the range occupies the area between the Syr Darya and Ili River. Huntington has described the Tien Shan as a plateau, with mountain structures and once with mountain form but long ago reduced to old-age flatness and only recently reuplifted. Erosion has thus been revived, especially around the margins.

This region is the most active earthquake area in the

Union. From 1885 to 1932, there were 24 shocks with an intensity over six.

Despite their distance from the sea, enormous glaciers descend from these ranges, notably the 48-mile Fedchenko glacier near the Trans-Alai Range. Numerous snow-capped peaks glisten in the clear air and make exceptionally beautiful views as seen from the near-by desert plains.

The climate is generally dry, with long periods of clear weather. Forests are limited to favored exposures with grass above and below. These upper and lower meadows are used for grazing sheep, horses, and cattle, with seasonal migration up and down the slopes. Lowland villages may be almost deserted during the summer while the flocks are on the upper slopes. While on the move, shepherds live in round felt-covered kibitkas, similar to Mongolian yurts. Agriculture is restricted to the lower valleys and usually depends on irrigation. Many of the canals are very old. Extensive upland areas are a cold desert, in contrast to the hot deserts of the lowlands.

Climatic limitations on agriculture increase with altitude, as shown in the Zeravshan Valley, where rice is cultivated to 4,000 feet, corn to 4,300 feet, peaches to 4,500 feet, grapes to 5,900 feet, millet to 6,400 feet, apricots to 6,900 feet, and barley to 8,200 feet.[1]

Two republics lie in these mountains, the Kirghiz S.S.R. in the east, and the Tadzhik S.S.R. to the south. In 1939, the former had a population of 1,459,301 while the latter had 1,485,091. Many of these people live in lowland valleys or bordering oases, to be considered in the following region.

Ancient caravan routes cross these mountains, though the passes are blocked by snow in winter. One famous route, followed by Marco Polo, leads over the Terek pass to the

[1] Berg, L. S., "The Natural Regions of the U.S.S.R.," Moscow and Leningrad (1937), 132.

Tarim Basin in China's westernmost province of Sinkiang; others go to Kashmir in northern India and to Afghanistan. Two historic routes farther north connect the Lake Balkhash area with Dzungaria in northwest China. One follows the Ili Valley, but the more famous is the Dzungarian Gate, a 46-mile gorge only 1,060 feet above sea level, between the Tarbagatai and the Dzungarian Alatau.

New automobile roads make the area more accessible. One leads from Frunze, capital of the Kirghiz Republic, past Lake Issyk Kul and Naryn over the Tien Shan to Osh at the head of the Fergana Valley. Passes exceed 12,000 feet. A second extends southward from Osh over a 9,850-foot pass in the Pamirs to Khorog on the Afghan frontier.

OASES OF SOUTHERN TURAN

From the Caspian to the frontiers of China and from the Pamirs to the borders of the agricultural land south of the Trans-Siberian, lie a million square miles of arid and semi-arid lowland. Much of it is uninhabitable desert except where mountain-nourished streams turn the waste into a garden. Within this area are two major geomorphic divisions, the Turan Lowland in the south, and the Kazakh Upland farther north. In terms of land use there are two geographic regions: the Aral-Balkhash Deserts and the Oases of Southern Turan.

Five Union republics cover this part of Soviet Middle Asia. The largest is the Kazakh Soviet Socialist Republic, with an area of 1,059,700 square miles and a 1939 population of 6,145,937. Parts of it extend westward into the Caspian Desert and northward into the West Siberian Agricultural Region.

Southwest of the Caspian Sea is the Turkmenian S.S.R., whose area is 171,250 square miles and whose population in

1939 was 1,253,985. Farther east is the Uzbek S.S.R., covering 146,000 square miles with 6,282,446 people. The Tadzhik and Kirghiz republics lie largely in the region of Pamir and Tien Shan Mountains.

Since the recognized homeland of the Turkmenians is confined to the southwest corner of Turan, the name Turkestan can no longer be applied to all of Soviet Middle Asia. Likewise the Kirghiz live in the mountains rather than in what has been called the Kirghiz Steppe in Kazakhstan.

This is an ancient land of great individuality and unusual history. For thousands of years, the struggle against aridity has dominated all of life and has concentrated settlement in the oases. Since rainfall is generally inadequate for agriculture, cultivation depends upon irrigation from mountain streams fed by melting snow. Each river has its local settlements in the midst of unreclaimed desert. Any regional boundary of the Turan Oases must include much barren land, but in general the region is an area of poor steppe grass with a semicontinuous sod in contrast to the barren desert farther north and west. Economic characteristics appear more significant than cartographic continuity.

The oases here considered follow the foothills from Mari, formerly Merv, in the west to Tashkent in the east. Other oases are so detached that they are best grouped with the desert region to follow. Mari is the chief settlement along the Murgab Valley, and one of the oldest cities of interior Asia. On the Amu Darya is Chardzhou, famed for the sweetness of its melons, with other towns upstream. Farther east is the historic Zeravshan Valley with the ancient cities of Bukhara and Samarkand, the latter with a population of 134,346 in 1939. Samarkand is especially famous for the monumental buildings that date from Tamerlane. Bukhara lies ten miles south of the Trans-Caspian Railway and is less modernized than Samarkand. Both cities were visited by the author in 1944 and were found to have much of the glamour with which they have been credited.

The upper Syr Darya waters the largest oasis of all in the valley of Fergana, surrounded by high mountains except for a six-mile opening on the west. The valley is 180 miles long by 100 miles wide, and supports the cities of Leninabad, formerly Khojent, Fergana, Khokand, and Osh. This is one of the most densely populated areas in the U.S.S.R., with an elaborate irrigation system. Tashkent lies on a tributary of the Syr Darya, the Chirchik; upstream is Chimkent. Tashkent is the industrial metropolis of Soviet Middle Asia with 585,005 people in 1939. Refugees from the war-invaded Ukraine raised the total to over a million in 1943.

After these streams leave the mountains, they receive no tributaries and grow progressively smaller through seepage, evaporation, and diversion for irrigation. Most of the small streams that enter the Fergana Valley never reach the Syr Darya. Even the sizable Zeravshan withers in the desert without entering the Amu Darya. No progressive climatic change is suggested since the river did not reach the Amu even in the fourth century B.C. Although rainfall is at a minimum in summer, melting snow and glaciers make this the season of maximum flow.

The volume of water and the irrigated area of the chief streams are shown in the accompanying table.[1] Ten acre-feet per acre are needed for satisfactory irrigation.

Most oases occupy alluvial fans between the mountains and the desert, at elevations from 1,000 to 1,500 feet above sea level. Rainfall is slightly higher than on the plains and ground water more abundant, so that there is a thin carpet of grass. As dust storms have swept across the desert through the centuries, silt has become trapped among this vegetation.

[1] DAVIS, ARTHUR P., Irrigation in Turkestan, *Civil Engineering*, II (1932), 2.

IRRIGATION IN TURAN

River	Annual discharge in acre-feet	Irrigated acreage
Amu Darya......................	53,200,000	1,100,000
Zeravshan......................	4,160,000	980,000
Syr Darya......................	15,000,000	2,190,000
Chirchik.......................	7,120,000	480,000

This wind-borne dust is the loess, the basis of extremely fertile soils.

The continentality of the climate is shown in the range between January and July means of over 55° F. for every

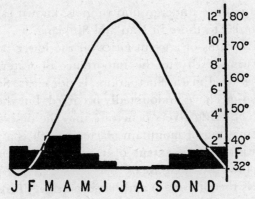

Tashkent is slightly more moist than other desert stations, owing to its elevation. Winter temperatures drop to a recorded minimum of −15° F. Elevation, 1,610 feet; average temperature, 56.1° F.; total precipitation, 14.7 inches.

station except Samarkand. Average July temperatures at Termez near Bukhara are the highest in the Union, with a maximum of 122° F. and a day and night average of 89.6° F. At Repetek, the sand temperature reached 174° F. on July 20, 1915. Thanks to the dry air, nights are cool. Cloudless summer skies increase the sugar content of grapes, melons, and apricots. Winters are severely cold, with temperatures sometimes near those of Leningrad. Since the edge of invading Siberian air masses is thin, cities on the plain may have lower temperatures than near-by mountains. The snow cover is light but persists for a month.

The precipitation is low and erratic. Tashkent averages 14.7 inches, which is considerably more than many stations. At Bukhara and Chardzhou the rainfall drops to 4 inches. Summers and falls are driest.

Many irrigation canals are centuries old and have been considerably expanded by new engineering works under the five-year plans. This is especially true in Fergana where water is brought to the dry side of the valley. Some of the ancient canals are underground tunnels, known as karez, or kanats, similar to those in Iran and Sinkiang.

Extensive ruins of ancient cities on the lower portions of dry waterways testify to the importance of water, but the evidence as to climatic fluctuations is not clear. Some rainfall fluctuations have undoubtedly occurred, but the distance to which withering rivers penetrate into the desert depends upon the melting of mountain glaciers which is a matter of summer warmth, the extent of upstream irrigation diversion, and the cultivated area.

Cotton is the chief crop and has been since the American Civil War when decreased supplies gave Russia the impetus to produce her own needs. The yield did not reach pre-revolutionary output until after 1930; of the cultivated acreage cotton now occupies two-thirds. Wheat, rice, and barley are the chief grains. Increasing amounts of cotton and some silk are woven in Middle Asia instead of being shipped to the Moscow textile area. Sugar beets are important since their sugar content is greatly increased under conditions of desert irrigation. These oases have long been renowned for their very fine fruit, such as apricots, peaches, cherries, plums, apples, melons, and grapes. The latter are dried as raisins.

Although mining has not been significant, considerable developments are under way. The Fergana Valley contains fair coal and some oil. The near-by mountains have copper, lead, zinc, gold, silver, and arsenic. Hydroelectric power is used to develop phosphate fertilizers. A steel mill was built at Tashkent during the Second World War.

Ancient crafts include the weaving of carpets, preparation of fur and leather, metal work, pottery, and the manufacture of saddles. Keen rivalries between the wandering nomads and sedentary oasis dwellers, as well as between rival oases, have often brought raids and destruction. Each oasis has its own history.

Samarkand lies on the Zeravshan River, whose water is so valuable that the name means "gold spreading." The city's origin is unknown, but it has been "a sparkling jewel enticing the hearts of Kings through the ages." Alexander the Great plundered the city in 329 B.C. In the eighth century it was the center of Arab culture, and in the thirteenth century it was conquered by Genghis Khan. When Tamerlane made it his capital in 1370, he built the brilliantly decorated mosques, tombs, and other buildings that still stand. Surrounding a central square, or Registan, are the monumental buildings of three ancient colleges, each decorated with enameled tiles of turquoise blue. At the beginning of the eighteenth century when there were almost no inhabitants, the city fell under Chinese control. Raiders from the deserts or mountains have often destroyed Samarkand, which has been as often rebuilt. The history and ruins of Bukhara are only slightly less impressive.

These oases are steppingstones along the ancient caravan route of inner Asia. This highway from Peking to the Mediterranean followed the foot of the mountains from one river to another and was in use long before the days of Marco Polo and recorded history. Along it flowed silk, furs, and art goods from China and India to Greece and Rome and Roman Britain. At Samarkand, Bukhara, and Merv, merchants of the Orient met traders of the Occident.

The oases of Southern Turan are inhabited by a wide variety of races, including Turkomens, Uzbeks, Persians, Tadzhiks, Kirghiz, Sarts, and Russians. The latter are newcomers, for Tashkent was not occupied until 1866 nor Bukhara till 1873.

It is difficult to evaluate current developments, because few outsiders have been permitted to study the region objectively since before the First World War. Sensitive frontier problems have made this true for a century. Even the 1914 Baedeker states that "Foreigners are not allowed to visit Turkestan except by special permission of the Russian Government. The traveler must send in his request . . . at the latest six months before the beginning of his journey."

ARAL-BALKHASH DESERTS

Here aridity dominates. The annual precipitation averages only 8 inches, in places but half that figure. Where it reaches 12 inches in the north, some precarious dry farming is attempted.

During the winter when the region is exposed to cold Siberian air, the average January temperature drops below freezing. The delta of the Amu Darya has recorded −14° F. In contrast to the imported winter weather, summer temperatures are the result of local insolation. Day and night temperatures in July average 80 to 85° F., which is hotter than the tropics.

Many rivers enter the region, but only a few have enough

water to cross the desert and those which do so end in salt lakes or playas. Whereas normal rivers in humid lands gain water from tributaries and flow *in* valleys, these streams lose water, become overloaded with sediment, and flow *on* their flood plain. Sand bars and shifting channels make navigation difficult.

The Aral and the Caspian seas were once connected by the dry course of the Uzboi River, later temporarily followed by the Amu Darya when it was deflected to the Caspian. Current irrigation proposals involve rediverting part of the Amu in order to reclaim additional desert land.

Although northern Kazakhstan has over 5,000 lakes, many of them are ephemeral. The major water bodies are the Aral Sea and Lake Balkhash. The former stands next to the Caspian as the second largest body of water in the Old World. A large part is only 30 to 60 feet deep, and the area fluctuates. Western Lake Balkhash is freshened by waters of the Ili River, while the eastern portion is salt from evaporation.

Within the region are several areas where geologic history, altitude, or climate introduces minor differences. The Kara Kum and Kizil Kum are sandy deserts on either side of the Amu Darya. Some of the shifting sand areas are said to be due to the destruction of the blanket of sparse vegetation by overgrazing or cultivation. Near the Syr Darya is the Golodnaya Steppe, slightly higher and more moist. The Bedpak Dala, or Hunger Steppe, lies north of the Chu River, while on the south shore of Lake Balkhash is the Semireche Steppe. In the north, the Kazakh Hills are a peneplained mountain range, often incorrectly termed the Kirghiz Steppe.

The soil is generally unleached serozem, a gray desert soil, with local salty or alkaline soils where ground water is close enough to the surface to permit evaporation of capillary moisture. The most prominent vegetation is the bushy saxaul.

Kazakhstan reported nine million cattle in 1936, some of which were in the agricultural region to the north. Most of the people live in oases, similar to those described in the previous region. Most nomads have now been collectivized. Hides, wool, meat, and grain are important exports. Astrakhan sheep are raised in the south. Great agricultural developments took place during the second war against Germany with labor supplied by farmers evacuated from Soviet Europe.

The discovery of mineral wealth has brought local mining developments, as at Karaganda, now the Union's third most important coal producer. Near the northern shore of Lake Balkhash is a great copper mine at Kounrad, with another development to the west at Djezkazgan. Sulphur is obtained north of Ashkhabad and lead at Chimkent near Tashkent.

The chief cities outside the semicontinuous oases belt are Ashkhabad in the southwest, capital of Turkmenia; Novo Urgench and Khiva on the lower Amu Darya; Frunze and Alma-Ata, capitals of the Kirghiz and Kazakh republics; Kazalinsk on the lower Syr Darya; Kounrad and its smelter town of Balkhash; and the coal city of Karaganda, population 165,937 in 1939.

Large areas of irrigated cotton are grown in the Uzbek Republic. (*Sovfoto*)

Modern irrigation works have reclaimed desert lands in Tadzhikistan. This dam is along the Vakhsh River. (*Sovfoto*)

Springless two-wheeled carts are widely used in the Turkmenian Republic.
(*Sovfoto*)

This camel caravan in the Uzbek Republic is carrying a load of rice, raised
on irrigated oasis land. (*Sovfoto*)

Golden eagles are used for hunting in the mountains of the Kirghiz Republic. (*Sovfoto*)

Kirghiz men and women are excellent horsemen, for they learn to ride as soon as they can walk. (*Sovfoto*)

The Turkmenian Republic has long been known for the quality of its rugs, made possible by high-grade wool. (*Sovfoto*)

Members of a collective farm in the Kirghiz Republic are listening to a native musical instrument known as the komuz. (*Sovfoto*)

WITHIN Siberia are five million square miles of northern Asia, much of it mountainous or cold or relatively inaccessible. Permanently frozen ground underlies three and three-quarters million square miles. Here is the world's greatest forest outside the equatorial selva, and the largest coal deposits outside North America. The Ob, Yenisei, Lena, and Amur are among the world's eight longest rivers.

But these details are only an introduction to Siberia. This is the last great pioneering land outside the tropics, and into it the Russians have gone and are going by the millions. Much of the thrill that characterizes Soviet socialism is associated with the cultivation of virgin land, the development of new mines and industries, the construction of new railways, and the growth of cities in Siberia. The environment places restrictions on the limits to which man may develop this land, but the potentialities are still enormous.

Transport is no longer limited to north-flowing rivers or to a single railway. The Trans-Siberian is double tracked, and the total railway mileage east of the Urals more than doubled in the interwar period. Airplane service has opened the north.

Under the three five-year plans more happened in Siberia than during the entire period since the Cossack leader Yermak crossed the Urals in 1580 and captured the village of Sibir on the Irtysh. Between 1914 and 1933, the population rose from 10,400,000 to 25,636,900, while cultivated land increased from 32,058 to 97,949 square miles. Siberia has 15

per cent of the Union's people and 12 per cent of the cultivated area.

WEST SIBERIAN AGRICULTURAL REGION

The surveyors who laid out the Trans-Siberian Railway
toward the close of the nineteenth century proved to be
practical geographers, for they placed it along what has become the continuation of the agricultural triangle. The railway alternately runs through the rich chernozem steppe and
the taiga forest.

The colonization of Siberia dates from 1580. As early set-
tlers pushed eastward, they kept within the empty forest or
along the northern edge of the grasslands to avoid conflict
with nomadic Mongol tribes. Travel was by boat as much
as possible, with short portages from the tributaries of the
Volga to those of the Ob, and in turn to the Yenisei, Lena,
and Amur.

The West Siberian Agricultural Region is one of the flattest areas on earth. Along the railway one travels 1,200 miles
from the Urals to the Yenisei scarcely seeing a hill. For hours
the landscape is as monotonous as an ocean voyage. The only
vantage points are church towers or grain elevators. Much
of the area is covered with Quaternary continental deposits,
beneath which are Tertiary marine sediments. Vast glacial
lakes left deposits that add to the flatness. Even the folded
strata of the Kazakh Hills have been worn down to low relief
and gentle slopes. In the steppeland south of the railway are
countless thousands of shallow depressions, sometimes filled
with lakes, which apparently represent wind scour during a
period of greater aridity.

Great annual variations characterize the temperature.
Winter snowfall is light, but bitter blizzards pile it into formidable drifts that disrupt railway traffic. Half the year is

below freezing, for average temperatures fall below that point in mid-October to remain until mid-April. The short summers have days that are uncomfortably warm, but average temperatures exceed 68° F. for only a month. Precipitation is from 12 to 18 inches, chiefly in the summer.

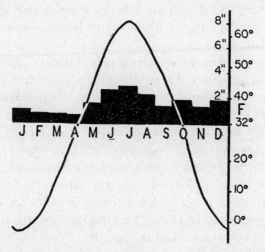

Tomsk is representative of climatic conditions in central Siberia with long and severe winters and moderate precipitation, half of which falls as snow. Elevation, 390 feet; average temperature, 30.2° F.; total precipitation, 19.9 inches.

This is the Asiatic continuation of two areas west of the Urals: the Central Agricultural Region of cleared forest with podsol soils, and the Southern Agricultural Region of cultivated steppe underlain by chernozem soils. Both landscapes are present in western Siberia, although most agricultural development has taken place in the steppe where there are no forests to be cleared and soils are more fertile. This is the tapering end of the cultivated triangle, pinched between limitations of cold on the north and of drought on the south, and limited eastward by the Altai, Sayan, and Baikal Mountains.

The great crop of the region is spring wheat, with large amounts of oats, rye, and barley. Huge grain elevators rise at every railway station and can be seen across the plain long before the town comes in sight. Flour milling is an important industry. This part of Siberia is an important cattle country, long famous for its export of butter. Meat packing is significant.

Siberian villages have surprisingly little in the way of commercial activities. Even settlements of several hundred houses have no store, for people live a nearly self-sufficient existence. Log houses are the rule in the north, replaced by sod houses where timber is not available. Each house has a huge brick stove which occupies nearly a quarter of the kitchen and which often has a platform on top where some of the family may sleep during the winter. Behind each house is usually a vegetable plot, with a barn for the farmer's own cow, pigs, and chickens. The rest of the cultivated land is collectivized and worked cooperatively.

Most of Soviet Siberia has a twofold economic pattern. The rivers provide a north-south orientation, while the railway is an east-west link. The West Siberian Agricultural Region is dominated by the railway, while the regions of the Ob, Yenisei, and Lena Taiga, shortly to be considered, are river-centered.

Where rail and water meet, significant cities develop. Since the Ob and Irtysh are the major rivers, Novosibirsk and Omsk are the leading cities, with populations in 1939 of 405,589 and 280,716, respectively. Krasnoyarsk on the Yenisei and Tomsk near the Ob follow in commercial significance, with 189,999 and 141,215. Industrialization and urban modernization generally decrease with distance from Moscow.

At these latitudes, rivers tend to be deflected to their right by the rotation of the earth; accordingly the eastern bank of these north-flowing rivers is often undercut and high, while the other is low and swampy. Approaching the rivers from the west, one finds a broad swampy flood plain, miles in width, which the railway crosses on an embankment rising to 50 feet or more in height. Then the river is crossed by a high bridge and the train at once enters a city on the right bank.

ALTAI-SAYAN MOUNTAINS

South-central Siberia is bordered by a continuation of the young mountains which begin in the Caucasus, continue through the Pamirs and Tien Shan, and reach northeastward to the Arctic. The Altai and Sayan ranges extend for a thousand miles from the Dzungarian Gate to near Lake Baikal. On a purely geologic basis, half the mountain area lies in Mongolia, but no geographically meaningful region can ignore a boundary such as that of the Soviets.

The region is mountainous but is important for mineral wealth rather than topography. Here is a third of the country's coal, lead, and zinc reserves. Deposits of silver, gold, copper, tin, and manganese are significant. Water-power possibilities along the Yenisei are impressive. Although much of the area is difficult of access, railway lines lead into the mining areas of Ridder, Kuznets, and Minusinsk.

Both the Altai and the Sayan were folded in the middle and late Paleozoic, then after being worn down to essential peneplains, were again uplifted during the late Tertiary. Metamorphic and intrusive rocks make a sequence difficult to unscramble. The central portions of the mountains remain rolling uplands above 10,000 feet, comparable to the Pamir and the Tien Shan, with active dissection on the margins.

The Altai system has a general northwest-southeast trend, which continues far into Mongolia. Several divisions may be distinguished within the Soviet Union. The Tarbagatai Range lies between the Dzungarian Gate and Lake Zaisan on the Irtysh. Between the Irtysh and Ob are the Altai Mountains proper, culminating in Mt. Belukha, 15,154 feet. Six glaciers radiate from this peak, one of them five miles long descending to an elevation of 6,400 feet. The snow line is from 8,000 to 10,000 feet. East of the Ob lie the eastern Altai, reaching almost to the Yenisei and formed of two north-south ranges, the Salair and the Kuznets-Alatau, respectively west and east of the Kuznets Basin.

Around the Minusinsk Basin are the two ranges of the Sayan system. The Eastern Sayan, with elevations up to 11,447 feet, is the main range, extending from Lake Baikal to the Yenisei, with a southern branch known as the Western Sayan along the frontier.

Neither the Kuznets nor the Minusinsk basin is level, and the rolling hills give the railways long steep grades. Around the Kuznets Basin is a flat sky line dating from the Mesozoic; the hilly margins carry a Tertiary surface, while the valley of the Tom River is Quaternary.

Steppe vegetation covers the lower slopes of the Altai-Sayan Mountains up to some 3,000 feet, above which there is a splendid taiga forest of Siberian larch, cedar, fir, pine, and birch to 6,000 feet or more, followed by alpine meadows to the snow line around 9,000 feet. Exact heights depend on exposure.

Rainfall at the foot of the mountains and in the basins does not exceed 10 inches but increases notably on the upper slopes. In the Western Sayans at 3,840 feet, the Olenya Creek station receives 47 inches, while in the Western Altai, the Andobin Mine with an elevation of 1,800 feet has 37 inches.

Summer is the rainy season, and the distant Atlantic is the apparent source of the moisture.

Winter temperature inversions, where the cold heavy air formed by radiation on the mountain slopes flows down into the valleys, combined with the thinness of the invading Siberian cold air masses, make the highlands a relatively warm island between the cold plains of Siberia and Middle Asia. The Minusinsk Basin, which receives cold air drainage from the surrounding mountains, has a January average of −5° F. and an extreme low of −65.7° F. These winter extremes along the upper Yenisei appear to be lower than at any other place on the river, even within the Arctic. July temperatures at Minusinsk average 69° F.

As the steppe grass is usually too short to be harvested, the original inhabitants were nomads moving about with their cattle and dwelling in felt-covered yurts. They now live in collectivized villages. Along the upper Tom and Yenisei rivers a quarter of the lowland is in wheat, potatoes, and sunflower. Large areas of virgin prairie are being plowed in the Minusinsk Basin. The chernozem soil is attractive but, with the breaking of the sod, dust-bowl conditions will develop in drier years.

Coal is the great mineral resource, with reserves of 450,-658,000,000 metric tons in the Kuznets Basin, and 20,612,-000,000 tons in the Minusinsk Basin. Along the northern margins of the region are the Chulym-Yenisei field with 43,000,000,000 tons, and the Kansk field with 42,000,000,000 tons. The Cheremkhovo mines west of Irkutsk also lie next to the Sayan Mountains, with reserves of 79,000,000,000 tons.

The Kuznets Basin is a closely folded syncline, with many beds dipping 60 to 80°. The carbon ratio is from 80 to 89 per cent, with sulphur at 0.5 per cent. Much of the coal is of coking quality, and some is suitable for gas and chemical use. Production amounted to 774,000 tons in 1913, 2,600,-

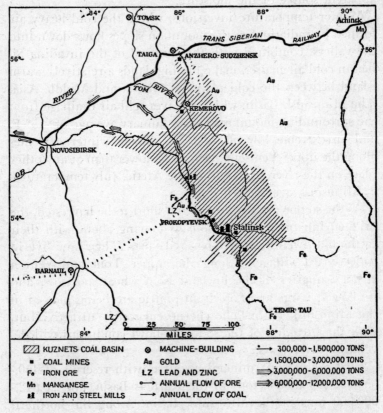

The Kuznets coal field is Siberia's principal center of heavy industry, developed with local coal and with iron ore from both the Urals and from local supplies in the mountains to the south around Temir Tau, known as the Gornaya Shoria.

Hunters are the chief residents of the vast taiga forests. This scene is north of Krasnoyarsk. (*Sovfoto*)

Excellent lumber is obtained from the virgin forests of the Far East. Transportation is facilitated by winter ice roads. (*Sovfoto*)

Bark wigwams provide homes for wandering Oirot nomads in the Altai Mountains of southern Siberia. (*Sovfoto*)

The Nentsi of the Taimyr Peninsula in the Arctic are relatives of the peoples in the mountains of southern Siberia; both keep reindeer. (*Northern Sea Route Administration*)

000 tons in 1927, and 16,800,000 tons in 1938. One mine at Prokopyevsk, completely electrified and mechanized, has a capacity of 3,200,000 tons annually. Other mining centers are Stalinsk, formerly named Kuznets, Leninsk-Kuznets, Kemerovo, and Anzhero-Sudzhensk.

Coal for urban and railway use is also mined on a small scale at Chernogorsk near Minusinsk, and at Cheremkhovo west of Irkutsk.

Surrounding the Kuznets Basin are several metal mines. Zinc, gold, and lead are obtained at Salair. Magnetite iron ore is mined in the Gornaya Shoria to the south, formed by metasomatic replacement of limestone, with an iron content of 45 per cent, but the high sulphur must be removed before smelting. Across the mountains in the Minusinsk Basin is excellent undeveloped ore 120 miles southwest of Abakan, which some day may be utilized with local coal.

In the metalliferous Altai at Ridder, southeast of Barnaul, are large lead and zinc plants, handling 1,000 tons of ore daily. This area, one of the country's oldest mining districts, also yields silver, gold, copper, and tin. Prehistoric people used bronze tools in their mining operations here.

Manganese occurs near Achinsk, but the ore contains only 20 to 25 per cent manganese in comparison with 50 per cent at Chiatury and 40 per cent at Nikopol. The annual output is 100,000 tons of ore.

At the beginning of the First Five-year Plan, it was recognized that heavy industry should not remain dependent upon Krivoi Rog and Donets. Iron was abundant in the Urals and coal occurred at Kuznets, but 1,419 miles of railway intervened. Because of the urgency of the problem and the flexibility of socialist finance, it was decided to inaugurate the Ural-Kuznets combine, with blast furnaces at each end of the line so that trains might carry ore or coal in either direction. Four huge blast furnaces and associated open-hearth works and rolling mills were built at both Magnitogorsk and Stalinsk. These plants are among the largest and most modern in the world, and each was laid out with daily capacity of 4,000 tons of pig iron. When they were visited in 1937, the Stalinsk production was the larger, but Magnitogorsk's capacity was higher.

Iron ore in the Kuznets area was then unknown, and Karaganda coal was undeveloped. This coal does not make as good coke as that from Kuznets, but it is only 600 miles from Magnitogorsk by a new direct railway. The enormous volume of rail shipment involved in the original combine is indicated by the freight traffic on the Trans-Siberian. Repeated counts on four trips in 1937 showed freight trains, all moving in the same direction and usually of 50 cars, every 17 minutes. The development of great steel works and associated industries in the midst of the empty Kuznets steppe is one of the major achievements of the Soviet Union. In 1937, 30 per cent of the iron ore was mined locally, with the rest from the Urals. Increasing development of near-by ore, plus the availability of Karaganda coal for the Ural plants, tends to make Kuznets an independent unit rather than part of the Ural-Kuznets combine as originally planned. This change is another illustration of the importance of completing the geological inventory before planning for major industrial programs.

Cities with smoking factories rise in the Kuznets Basin as abrupt and exotic intrusions in a treeless land scarcely inhabited even by nomads before the First World War. The city of Stalinsk, whose railway station is still named Kuznets, had 169,538 people in 1939. Near-by Prokopyevsk reported 107,227, while Kemerovo had 132,978. The urban population of the Kuznets area and Novosibirsk exceeds 1,000,000.

OB TAIGA

The history of Siberia is the history of her rivers, modified by railroads during the present century. Although the major streams flow across the main line of travel to the east, early travelers used a series of portages to link the tributaries into a water route to the Pacific. The headwaters of the Kama, a Volga tributary, cross the Urals; from there it is a short portage to the tributaries of the Tobol in the Ob system. The Chulym, which enters the Ob from the east, flows within six miles of the Yenisei. By following up a Yenisei tributary, the Angara, to near Lake Baikal, one may either cross to the Amur system or travel via the Lena on toward the Sea of Okhotsk. The Ob was the first Siberian river to be developed and still has better steamers and more freight than the others.

The flatness of the West Siberian Plain is shown in the gradient of the Ob. At a distance of 1,850 miles from its mouth, the elevation is only 308 feet, a slope of but two inches per mile. Although the plain continues from the Urals eastward beyond the Yenisei to the edge of the Central Siberian Uplands, the geographic region ends near the left bank of the Yenisei.

The Ob has a length of 3,200 miles and is joined by the Irtysh which in turn receives the Ishim and Tobol. The length of rivers navigable at high water in the Ob system totals 19,200 miles, of which two-thirds are in use. Nearly half the freight, chiefly grain and timber, is carried on the Irtysh, navigable into Sinkiang. The river is free from ice 175 days at Tobolsk and 153 days at Salekhard, formerly Obdorsk, near the gulf. Near Tobolsk, winter ice is 30 to 40 inches thick, at Salekhard, 40 to 60 inches.

The Ob Taiga has a typical boreal climate, *Dc* in Koeppen symbols. Winters are long with a considerable snow cover. The annual precipitation is about 18 inches, decreasing to 14 inches near the Arctic.

The coniferous forest resembles that of the Dvina-Pechora Taiga in general, but lower rainfall, a more severe winter, and poor drainage change many species. Siberian fir predominates, mixed with white-barked trees such as birch and aspen. The Vasyugan Swamp covers 100,000 square miles near the junction of the Ob and Irtysh. Timber is shipped from Salekhard, usually consigned to Arkhangelsk rather than abroad. Very large amounts move upstream to the Trans-Siberian Railway for urban and industrial needs.

There are few cities of significance, and many place names shown on maps are riverside clearings of a few dozen houses. Large areas are completely without settlement, inaccessible in summer because of swamps and mosquitoes. Contact with the rest of the Union is chiefly through cities to the south where the railway taps the Ob, Irtysh, or other tributaries.

YENISEI TAIGA

From the source of the Yenisei to the ocean is 2,619 miles but, if the distance be measured along its major tributary, the Angara, and its extensions beyond Lake Baikal, the length is 3,553 miles. Fourth among the world's rivers in length, the Yenisei ranks seventh in drainage area with over a million square miles. The river lies at the latitude of the Mackenzie in Canada, placing Krasnoyarsk on the parallel of Edmonton, and Igarka at the same distance beyond the Arctic Circle as Aklavik.

Most of the Yenisei Taiga is within the Central Siberian Upland, particularly the Tunguska Platform where hills gradually rise to an elevation of 4,500 feet along the Lena divide. From these uplands the Yenisei receives three major tributaries. In the south the Verkhne or Upper Tunguska, commonly called the Angara, flows out of Lake Baikal. In the middle is the Podkamena or Stony Tunguska, while the northern tributary is the Nizhni or Lower Tunguska.

Virgin forest extends from south of the Angara 750 miles northward to beyond Igarka. This taiga is a trackless expanse of conifers and whitewoods. Toward the south, and especially along the Angara, are splendid stands of commercial pine, but adverse conditions in the north reduce the trees to less than a foot in diameter. These forests are so vast that only preliminary studies have been possible, but estimates in the Yeniseisk-Igarka area run to 167 billion board feet of lumber. Conifer reserves along the Angara are three times this figure.

The taiga is usually described as a coniferous forest of fir and pine, but airplane flights by the writer over the Yenisei have revealed that birch and deciduous softwoods cover a third of the area.

Sawmills are in operation at Krasnoyarsk, Maklakova, Yeniseisk, and Igarka, with an overseas export from the latter city of 90 million board feet in 1937. In addition to 18 shiploads sent to England, Holland, and Germany, three vessels carried lumber from the Yenisei to southeastern Africa in that year.

Permanently frozen ground underlies almost the entire region. Summer heat thaws the ground to a depth of three or four feet beneath the insulating forest, or as deep as ten feet on cleared ground.

The Tunguska Platform contains enormous reserves of coal, known along the rivers and thought to continue between them. Tentative estimates reach 400 billion tons. Local intrusions of trap sheets have altered the coal to graphite, mined since 1862. At Norilsk in the Arctic, nickel, copper, lead, zinc, and coal are mined.

The Yenisei system is the great unifier of the region, for all settlement is along waterways. Four dozen boats operate on the river, a quarter of them with passenger accommodations. Regular steamboat lines operate from the railway at Krasnoyarsk, going south in three days to Minusinsk, north in six days to Igarka, and in eight days to Dudinka. Through most of the region the river is over a mile in width; depths exceed 50 feet except in the estuary.

Russians reached the lower Yenisei via the Arctic in 1610, whereas overland travelers from Tomsk did not see the Yenisei until Yeniseisk was established in 1618.

The most interesting city of the Yenisei Taiga is also the newest, Igarka, which provides a sheltered anchorage where cargoes can be transferred between river and ocean vessels. Though within the Arctic Circle, it lies 400 miles inland from the shallow and stormy estuary. In 1929 Igarka was a settlement with one house and three people; by 1937 its population numbered 15,000. The largest lumber mills east of the Urals cut logs floated down from the Angara for shipment during the two-month navigation period in August and September when the Kara Sea is open. To keep people healthy, fresh vegetables are raised in greenhouses and on open fields. Root crops do well, and leafy vegetables are reasonably successful, but grain does not ripen. Four hundred cows supply fresh dairy products and animal manure that is essential for field use if crops are to grow.

ARCTIC FRINGE

Although the Arctic might not appear the most attractive part of the Soviet Union, there are few other regions whose development has met with equal enthusiasm. Nearly half the Arctic lands of the earth lie within the U.S.S.R., and no other country has given so much attention to the development of northern latitudes.

Interest in northern Siberia and a possible northeast passage to China dates from the middle of the sixteenth century when the Spanish and Portuguese dominated the route around Africa so that the Dutch and English tried to sail via the north of Asia. Sebastian Cabot sent out an expedition in 1553 with instructions to "use all wayes and meanes possible to learn how men may passe from Russia either by land or by sea to Cathaia." Henry Hudson was another who explored this route, but neither expedition was able to sail east of Nova Zemlya.

Russian merchant adventurers sailed to the mouth of the Ob and founded a trading post in 1608, but the fear of foreign penetration led the Czar to forbid all Arctic navigation in 1624. Modern commerce reached the Yenisei again under Nordenskjöld in 1875, and in 1878-1879 he made the first voyage to the Pacific. During the Russo-Japanese War, 22 ships were sent to the mouth of the Yenisei to relieve traffic on the railway.

Soviet activities on an extensive scale date from 1932 when the icebreaker *Sibiriakov* made the first voyage from Arkhangelsk to Vladivostok in a single season. Under the Northern Sea Route Administration, regular services operate to the various rivers and a dozen or more vessels make the complete transit each summer. Icebreakers and scouting airplanes are used in the most difficult areas. Freight through Kara Sea ports, chiefly Igarka, increased from 10,000 tons in 1920 to 137,460 in 1935. Lena freight in 1935 amounted to 13,000 tons. Service to the Kolyma River and points eastward is usually routed via Vladivostok, with 16,000 tons of freight in 1935. Except for exports of Yenisei lumber, most goods are consigned inward. The 1937 total Arctic freight amounted to 250,000 tons. Very large quantities of American lend-lease aid moved via the Arctic during the early 1940's.

Four groups of islands divide the Soviet Arctic into five seas. The chief ports of the Barents Sea are Murmansk and Arkhangelsk. Ice forms early in October, reaching its maximum thickness and extent at the end of April. The Murmansk coast remains ice-free owing to the Atlantic drift. To the east of the Barents Sea are the two islands of Nova Zemlya, or new land, separated by the narrow Matochkin Strait, ice-free for four months but fogbound for 19 days each month. Alternate passages lead north or south of the islands.

The Kara Sea is bounded on the east by Severnaya Zemlya, or north land. Ice forms a month earlier and persists a month longer than in the Barents Sea. Both the Ob and the Yenisei have broad estuaries with sand bars where the depth of water is 16 and 23 feet, respectively. On the Ob, the chief river port is Salekhard, but most ocean vessels must unload at Novi Port in the estuary, where there is a floating wharf two miles from the shore. At the mouth of the Yenisei, barren Dickson Island has a good harbor but cannot be reached by river boats, so that transshipment takes place at Igarka. Dudinka is also developing a port for near-by Norilsk coal and nickel.

The Laptev or Nordenskjöld Sea occupies the section from Severnaya Zemlya to the New Siberian Islands. Its chief port is Tiksi Bay in the Lena Delta, where a ten-foot sand bar blocks ocean vessels. Shipping also calls at Nordvyk on the Khatanga River where there is a small production of salt and petroleum.

The East Siberian Sea is so shallow that navigation is difficult. Sand bars at the mouths of the Kolyma and Indigirka necessitate transshipment in the open sea. On the east the sea terminates at Wrangel Island, around which ice conditions are the worst of the entire passage. The Chukchee Sea continues to Bering Strait.

To supplement the steamer services, an air line was inaugurated in 1940 from Moscow to Arkhangelsk, Igarka, Tiksi, and the Chukotsk Peninsula, 4,500 miles distant.

Even though the navigation period is short and the hazards considerable, there is strategic value in a protected route from Murmansk to Vladivostok. The naval significance is uncertain, but in comparison the Russian fleet was obliged to sail around Africa in 1905 and arrived in Japanese waters quite unprepared for combat. Like the United States, the Union of Soviet Socialist Republics is a two-ocean country and the Northern Sea Route may become the Soviets' Panama Canal.

The Soviet Union claims ownership of all land in the sector north to the Pole. In 1937-1938, a scientific station occupied the North Pole, where the ocean depth was found to be 14,075 feet.

Wandering hunters and fishermen spend the summers in birch-bark wigwams along the streams where they catch and dry fish, while the winter months are devoted to trapping. Many Mongoloid peoples are represented, some of them similar to nomads who also keep reindeer in the Sayan Mountains in the south. The names Samoyed and Tungus were formerly used for groups who should now be termed Nentsi and Evenki. Formerly without a written language, they have been given an alphabet. Schools, medical centers, and reindeer-breeding stations have been provided.

Surface travel across the tundra is difficult during the brief summer, for there are innumerable swamps and lakes. According to a native saying, "there are as many lakes as there are stars in the sky."

Normal agriculture is almost impossible, but most Russian commercial and scientific outposts have experimental gardens and greenhouses. On Dickson Island electricity generated by the wind is used to light and heat underground greenhouses.

Conditions near the southern margin of the tundra are illustrated by Dudinka, an old settlement of 2,500 and the administrative and commercial center for the Taimyr Okrug. In 1936, the fur catch was valued at 4,800,000 rubles, and two tons of ivory from ice-age mammoths were shipped. The frost-free period averages less than 60 days; in 1937, from June 24 to August 18. The temperature dropped to −42° F. on Feb. 28, 1937, and the monthly average was −9° F. Every month has from 64 to 87 per cent cloudiness. Precipitation amounts to 9 inches, almost entirely in the late summer.

The Northern Sea Route Administration is a modern East India or Hudson's Bay Company. It is not only in charge of navigation, but to it is entrusted the economic development of all land north of latitude 62° N. Hundreds of millions of rubles have been spent in developing the tundra and northern taiga. Hundreds of weather stations are linked by radio, and air mass weather maps are prepared each six hours at the chief flying centers. The challenging pioneer spirit of the Soviets is nowhere better exhibited than in their conquest of the Arctic.

BAIKALIA

Lake Baikal imposes a barrier to all east-west travel in southern Siberia. High mountains along the near-by Mongolian frontier force the railway to follow the margin of the lake where it is necessary to blast a shelf at the edge of the water. Farther north the Stanovoi Mountains continue to the Lena Valley. When approaching Baikalia from the west, the Yenisei Ridge and Eastern Sayan Mountains restrict travel to the Krasnoyarsk gateway, so that the only feasible route is by way of Irkutsk.

The lake occupies a graben that makes it the deepest lake in the world, 5,712 feet. Surrounding mountains are over a mile high; hence the fault displacement is 10,700 feet. A severe earthquake in 1861 indicates the sensitive nature of the geology. In area, Lake Baikal is in eighth place among the world's lakes, but in volume it ranks first, even containing more water than the Caspian Sea. The Selenga is the chief of its tributaries, while the Angara forms the only outlet.

The geographic region of Baikalia lies largely to the east of the lake. Confused mountain structures trend northeast-southwest, and include the Pre-Baikal, Trans-Baikal, Yablonovi, and Olekminsk-Stanovik ranges. Much of the region is formed of crystalline and metamorphic rocks, with elevations over a mile.

The climate appears to represent the furthermost penetration of summer monsoon winds from the Pacific. The maximum temperature of the water in Lake Baikal is delayed until August, and freezing does not occur until January. As a result, the shores have but 90 days below 14° F., while there are 140 such days elsewhere near by. In summer, the vicinity of Baikal has 70 days with an average of 50° or over, as compared with 100 such days elsewhere. Fishing is important.

Most of Baikalia is covered by a pine forest, with Mongolian-type steppe in the drier lowlands. Cultivated land totals one and a half million acres. Many of the people are Buriats, who specialize in cattle raising.

East of Lake Baikal is coal, and iron is produced in an enlarged plant at Petrovsk. The region also has numerous occurrences of tin, tungsten, zinc, gold, arsenic, and molybdenum. Prospective developments center around water power, coal, and iron ore west of Irkutsk under the project known as Angarastroi. This may some day be one of the leading industrial centers of the Soviet Union.

The Trans-Siberian Railway links the three major cities. Irkutsk lies on the swift-flowing Angara, 44 miles from Lake Baikal, and had a population of 243,380 in 1939. Ulan-Ude, formerly Verkhne Udinsk, is at the crossing of the Selenga, the junction for a railway south to the Mongolian People's Republic, and has a large meat-packing plant. Chita lies near the railway junction to Manchuria.

LENA TAIGA

Two features of the Lena Valley are of special interest: great gold production and the new railway north of Lake Baikal.

Gold has been obtained from the rivers of the northeast for many decades, and early in the twentieth century was exploited by a large British concession named Lena Goldfields. Production greatly expanded with the discovery of the Aldan fields in 1923 where placer and lode deposits contribute a fifth of the country's gold. The new town of Aldan, formerly Nezametny, has a population of 4,000 and near-by mining camps raise the number of people in the Aldan district to 40,000. An automobile road leads south to the Trans-Siberian Railway at Bolshoi Niever. Bodaibo is also an important producer.

The Lena River has long been handicapped because its headwaters were not reached by the Trans-Siberian. Although the river runs within six miles of Lake Baikal, rugged mountains intervene. This has been changed by the construction of a new railway around the north of Lake Baikal toward the Pacific, which reaches the Lena at Kirensk. Much secrecy surrounded the construction of this Baikal-Amur Railway because of its military significance in case of a Far Eastern war. Although construction started in 1937 and at

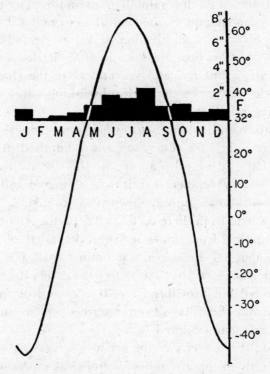

The climate of Yakutsk is of the extreme continental type, with a range of 112° F. in the January to July monthly average, and an extreme range of 186° F. Elevation, 330 feet; average temperature, 12.2° F.; total precipitation, 13.7 inches.

one time was pressed with great effort, it appears that the line was not completed in 1945.

The climate is the driest and coldest of any Siberian region yet considered. Precipitation is from 6 to 12 inches, and snowfall amounts to little over a foot. Yearly temperature averages are below freezing, so that a continental ice sheet might develop were there enough snowfall. There is no evidence of Pleistocene glaciation. The Lena is frozen at Yakutsk for 210 days.

On account of the low rainfall, grasslands replace the taiga in the lowland plains of the central Lena and Viloui, with resulting black soils. Cultivation is only moderately successful, but 225,000 acres were sown in 1935. Barley and wheat can be raised, but hay and vegetables are the chief crops. Most of the native population live by fishing, gathering furs, and raising reindeer.

Navigation on the Lena began when a steamer was brought from Norway in 1878. There are now a hundred steamships and launches. In order to appreciate the size of this region, it is well to remember that it is a thousand miles from Kirensk on the new railway down river to Yakutsk, and another thousand from there to Tiksi Bay on the Arctic Ocean. Coal is supplied from mines at Sangarkhai north of Yakutsk and at Kangalass. Production amounted to 30,000 tons in 1932 and was to reach 250,000 tons by 1942. Reserves are unprospected but probably large. It is typical of Soviet enthusiasm that these have been described as "inexhaustible reserves, as yet unexplored."

Yakutsk, the one city of importance, serves as the capital for the million square miles of the Yakut Autonomous Soviet Socialist Republic. Founded in 1632, it had a population of 27,000 in 1935. Like other Siberian towns, it has broad muddy streets, plank sidewalks, and one-story log houses, plus a few old brick buildings. The city is poorly located on a low terrace at the inside of a bend on a shallow branch of the Lena. The river, here full of islands and 15 miles wide, is shifting away from the town so that boats must unload four miles distant at low water. Floods frequently inundate the city.

NORTHEASTERN MOUNTAINS

This region continues the system of young mountains that cross central Eurasia from the Alps to Kamchatka. This corner of the Union is so inaccessible that the Cherski Range, rising to 9,843 feet, was not discovered until 1926. Kamchatka has the greatest group of volcanoes on the continent, with 127 cones of which 19 are active. The highest is Mt. Kliuchevskaya, 15,950 feet, which has erupted 19 times in two centuries. In 1907, the volcano Shtiubelia ejected four billion cubic yards of ashes, and some of the dust fell in Europe.

The Northeastern Mountains have long been known as the icebox of the world. No inhabited place has observed so low minima as Verkhoyansk and Oimekon. Extreme low temperatures are not related to the winter high pressure over Siberia but are due to intense radiation in calm air and local air drainage into enclosed basins. Verkhoyansk has a January average of −59° F. and an absolute minimum of −90° F. Observations at Oimekon since 1928 show that winters are consistently colder, so that it may replace Verkhoyansk as the coldest station. The unattractive character of the Oimekon district is indicated by its population of 565 households or 2,400 people in an area of 27,000 square miles.

In 1916, all of this region was regarded as outside the limits of possible cultivation. Agricultural experiment stations have shown that some vegetables may be grown in the southern half, especially in the central valley of Kamchatka. Most of the region has as little precipitation as the Aral-Balkhash Desert, but monsoon winds bring 40 inches to the southeastern part of Kamchatka. Elsewhere mountain tundra replaces taiga forest.

The Okhotsk Sea and the waters around Kamchatka have

long been important fishing grounds. Since the catch must be sun dried, the cloudy and foggy weather of summer presents problems. From 1847 to 1871, American whalers secured whale oil and bone here to the value of $87,500,000; and whales are still caught. Under the Treaty of Portsmouth which ended the Russo-Japanese War of 1904-1905, Japanese fishermen were given special concessions in this area, and the gradual restriction of these arrangements has been the source of much political friction. Salmon, cod, herring, and crab are caught. The chief port on Kamchatka is Petropavlovsk, founded in 1741 and located on one of the world's finest harbors. The port is the most important Soviet harbor on the open Pacific.

The mining of gold on the upper Kolyma started in 1929, and an automobile road leads south to the new town of Magadan at Nagaevo Bay on the Sea of Okhotsk.

THE FAR EAST

Southeastern Siberia borders the Pacific and is significant as the frontier toward Japan. The Third Five-year Plan emphasized the military importance of agricultural and industrial developments, and assigned four billion rubles or 4 per cent of its funds to the political units known as the Khabarovsk and Maritime territories, which include all of the Pacific margin to the Arctic. The geographic region here considered is essentially the Amur Basin, plus Sakhalin.

The decade prior to the Second World War was marked by a great increase in cultivated land, the beginnings of heavy industry, the growth of cities, and active immigration which brought the population to over two million. With the empty spaces coming into use, the Far East is now self-sufficient in its food and in many of its industrial needs.

The Amur is the great river of the east, comparable to

Large herds of seals inhabit the Komandorski Islands off Kamchatka.
(*Sovfoto*)

The Northern Sea Route is kept open by powerful icebreakers. Navigation
in most sections is limited to less than three months. (*Sovfoto*)

This is a street in Birobidjan, the Jewish Autonomous Region in the Far East. (*Sovfoto*)

Sugar beets have become an important crop in the Ussuri and Amur valleys around Khabarovsk. (*Sovfoto*)

the three north-flowing rivers. The chief tributaries on the left bank are the Zeya and Bureya, while on the right the Sungari comes from Manchuria, and the Ussuri forms the eastern Manchurian border. Along the central Amur around Khabarovsk is a broad plain which continues up the Ussuri

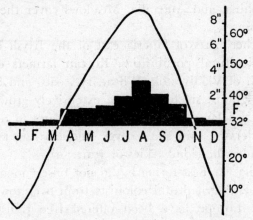

Vladivostok lies near the limits of the Pacific monsoon, with maximum precipitation during the summer months. Elevation, 50 feet; average temperature, 39.7° F.; total precipitation, 14.7 inches.

to Lake Khanka. On the east, the Amur plain is enclosed by the Sikhota Alin Mountains, while on the west are the Little Khingan Mountains. West of this is the Bureya-Zeya plain, limited by the extension of the Great Khingan Mountains.

The Far East has a continental climate modified by the Pacific monsoons. Strong dry winter winds blow from the interior, with temperatures far below freezing. In summer, relatively warm oceanic air imports moisture, bringing an annual rainfall of 25 inches to Vladivostok. Although Vladivostok lies in the latitude of southern Crimea, its east coast position gives winter temperatures 45° F. colder, resembling Halifax.

The flora is of the Manchurian type, with magnificent stands of Korean pine, spruce, fir, and larch, mixed with 10 per cent of deciduous forms such as oak. Timber not only supplies the expanding internal market but is shipped to Japan, China, and Australia. Meadows cover the drier interior basins.

Few other parts of Siberia east of the Irtysh have such good agricultural possibilities. Korean farmers even raise rice north of Vladivostok. Wheat, rye, oats, and barley are the chief grains; sugar beets are extensively grown. Spring planting is delayed since the ground freezes to ten feet or more under the thin snow cover, and thawing takes place slowly under the cloudy skies of June.

Since the Far East formerly did not raise enough food to supply itself, agricultural colonists from overcrowded parts of Soviet Europe have been offered free transportation, credits, and tax exemption. The Jewish colony of Birobidjan, west of Khabarovsk, is especially interesting. Jews receive full rights throughout the U.S.S.R. but have heretofore had no district that was exclusively their own. This Soviet Palestine provides such a haven and at the same time strengthens the regional economy.

When the Trans-Siberian Railway was built to Vladivostok late in the nineteenth century, the line cut across Manchuria via the Chinese Eastern Railway. As the subsequent war with Japan stressed the desirability of an all-Russian route, the Amur line was constructed. To avoid proximity to the Chinese frontier, the railway runs through very difficult terrain some tens of miles north of the Amur River. The new Baikal-Amur Railway will open new country near the Stanovoi Mountains and provide a second route to the Pacific, of more strategic than economic significance for the present.

The Far East has mineral resources for a growing industry. Steel mills have been built at Komsomolsk to use Buryea coal and iron ore from either the Little Khingan or lower Amur, both of low grade. Lead and zinc have long been secured along the Japan Sea. The chief oil production east of the Urals is in Sakhalin.

Komsomolsk is the magic city of the east. Although founded only in 1932, its population reached 70,000 by 1939. This is the "city of youth," the lodestone of enthusiastic workers from all over the Union. Situated on the lower Amur, it has the largest steel mills and shipyards in the Soviet Far East.

Khabarovsk has developed where the Trans-Siberian Railway spans the Amur. It is the political and commercial center of the area, with a population of 199,364 in 1939.

Vladivostok has a picturesque setting on Peter the Great Bay. The city's trade increased greatly during the First and Second World Wars and during periods of favorable political relations with Manchuria. The harbor is kept open throughout the year by icebreakers. Coal is secured from near-by bituminous deposits. The population numbered 206,432 in 1939.

The Far East offers considerable promise. Soils and climate make agriculture relatively attractive. Timber reserves are excellent, minerals fairly abundant, and transportation rapidly improving. Many of the people are pioneers, and this "new east" resembles Canada's "great west." But neither Canada nor the Soviet Union is primarily a Pacific power, nor can either escape its cold.

GEOSTRATEGY AND THE FUTURE OF THE UNION

THE greatness of a nation rests upon many interrelated factors. Some of these are physical, some human. Despite poor soil and unfavorable location, many countries have created a rich civilization often because of a few great leaders or a system of government. History and geography provide a changing panorama, and the elements that brought greatness in one century may have different significance in another. Even environmental factors may change, as with new air-age accessibility or with improved crops that will mature in colder areas and thus shift the agricultural frontier.

It is now clear that the Soviet Union has emerged as one of the great powers of the twentieth century. Credit for this achievement goes in part to a dynamic political and social system and in part to the basic geographical factors of minerals and position. The fundamental natural resources of a weak czarist Russia were the same as those of a strong Soviet Union, but something new has been added. What then are the factors in Soviet strength? This chapter is a consideration of political geography and its application to the future prospects of the U.S.S.R.

No other nation in Eurasia has so many resources or such a large area. China is more populous and Germany has been more aggressive, but no other power holds the same assets of minerals and location. How it makes use of these assets is another matter. These opportunities bring corresponding responsibilities.

The Soviet Union is too big to study on a flat map; only a globe is adequately honest. Mercator maps do not show that the great-circle course from New York to Chungking runs directly over the North Pole and across Siberia, or that the shortest route from Shanghai to London cuts far to the north of Leningrad.

Geographic understanding is vital for an adequate appreciation of world problems, and geographic ignorance is immeasurably expensive. This understanding is not in itself a solution for postwar problems, but without it no sure peace can prevail. Here is a continent far larger than any in terms of which Americans have ever thought before.

THE HEARTLAND IDEA

The vast spaces of Asia have been a favorite field for writers in political geography. Unfortunately many of them have understood too little the geography of the continent which they have been considering, and have failed to think adequately in terms of a round world in the age of the air.

Many of these discussions have centered around the relative military importance of land power versus sea power. Does command of the ocean with its resulting world-wide access to raw materials ensure ultimate victory over land-based nations, or can large continental areas be made into a secure fortress? Many older conclusions are now invalidated with the arrival of three-dimensional war and the ability of the airplane to surmount barriers of seacoast, mountains, or jungle.

In 1904, Sir Halford J. Mackinder, a distinguished English political geographer, pointed out that the three continents of Europe, Asia, and Africa constitute one great cultural, political, and economic "World Island"; around it the lesser land areas are grouped in relatively minor importance.

Geostrategy and the Future of the Union

Within this larger area is a core or "Heartland" in the northern interior of Eurasia. The essential feature of this area is inaccessibility from the ocean, and hence from naval power. The area extends from the Arctic Coast to the central deserts and mountains, and westward to the broad isthmus between the Baltic and Black seas. The Heartland thus includes the bulk of the U.S.S.R., all except the Pacific fringe and the west, and also Mongolia, Sinkiang, Tibet, Afghanistan, and most of Iran. The most developed part of the Union, namely, the widest end of the essential fertile triangle, lies largely outside the Heartland. The mere fact that the latter includes the bulk of the Soviet's total area in square miles does not imply that the two are synonymous in economic meaningfulness. The western Heartland boundary is the only one not marked by physical features, and Mackinder variously placed the limit at the Volga or at the western borders of Russia. Only from the west is the Heartland approachable; hence the strategic importance of eastern Europe.

Mackinder was impressed with the fact that the basis of world politics is essentially a struggle between sea power and land power, and that his Heartland could withstand indefinite siege. The oceanic peoples of western peninsular Europe have for centuries dominated the landsmen of Africa and Asia. On the other hand, he said in 1919, "must we not still reckon with the possibility that a large part of the Great Continent might some day be united under a single sway, and that an invincible sea-power might be based upon it; that is the great ultimate threat to the world's liberty. . . ." [1] Maritime Europe should thus be opposed to whatever power attempts to organize the resources of eastern Europe and the interior of Eurasia.

[1] MACKINDER, HALFORD J., "Democratic Ideals and Reality," New York: Holt (1919), 70.

This led him to the conclusion that "the World Island and Heartland are the final geographical realities in regard to sea-power and land-power, and that East Europe is essentially a part of the Heartland."[1] Thus there is a conflict between west and east Europe; one oceanic, the other with access to the continent. Summing up Mackinder's concepts, his most widely quoted statement was

> *Who rules East Europe commands the Heartland.*
> *Who rules the Heartland commands the World-Island.*
> *Who rules the World-Island commands the World.*[2]

These ideas are best stated in his volume just cited, which was written at the end of the First World War as a warning to the peacemakers concerning the necessity of securely enclosing Germany on the east. Should German technical and military skill ever unite with Russian space and resources, the combination would become unbeatable. Sea power, pointed out Mackinder, can outflank land power and draw on distant supplies through command of the ocean, but it needs an adequate home base. Land power can win in the long run, however, if it has resources, location, and size. Mackinder wrote as a Britisher, impressed with the importance of a navy but unaware of the mobility of modern operations or the future of air power in a world where old barriers disappear. He recognizes that Britain's home base is too small and too vulnerable to modern attack, but he overestimates the advantages of his Heartland. He also fails to point out that America enjoys both the maritime assets of western Europe plus citadel security.

Mackinder restated his views in 1944 as follows: "All things considered, the conclusion is unavoidable that if the Soviet Union emerges from this war as conqueror of Ger-

[1] *Ibid.*, 139.
[2] *Ibid.*, 150.

many, she must rank as the greatest land power on the globe. Moreover, she will be the Power in the strategically strongest defensive position. The Heartland is the greatest natural fortress on earth. For the first time in history it is manned by a garrison sufficient both in number and quality. Some persons today seem to dream of a global air power which will 'liquidate' both fleets and armies. I am impressed, however, by the broad implications of a recent utterance of a practical airman: 'air power depends absolutely on the efficiency of its ground organization.' It can only be said that no adequate proof has yet been presented that air fighting will not follow the long history of all kinds of warfare by presenting alternatives of offensive and defensive tactical superiority, meanwhile effecting few permanent changes in strategical conditions." [1]

Two other writers have had a large influence on the ideas of the German school of political geography. During the late nineteenth century, the distinguished German geographer Friedrich Ratzel developed the theory that the state is an organism with laws of growth which require ever-increasing living room, or *lebensraum*. Only as it grows and expands can it live. He maintained "that every people has to be educated from smaller to larger space conceptions; and that the process has to be repeated again and again to prevent people from sinking back into old small space conceptions." [2]

Rudolf Kjellen, a Swedish professor of history and government, borrowed Ratzel's laws of growth and was the first to apply the term Geopolitik. Geopolitics, states Kjellen, "is the theory of the state as a geographic organism or phenomenon in space, *i.e.*, as land, territory, area, or, most pregnantly,

[1] WEIGERT, HANS W., and VILHJALMUR STEFANSSON, "Compass of the World," New York: Macmillan (1944), 168.

[2] KALIJARVI, THORSTEN V., "Modern World Politics," New York: Crowell (1942), 611.

as country (*reich*)." [1] It has been said by Lin Yu-tang that German "geopolitics is fifty per cent factual data, thirty per cent pseudo-science and twenty per cent German metaphysics or 'Faustian Longing.' " [2] This has given the word a distinctive connotation, but there is no reason why the valid ideas of political geography may not continue to be examined under the simpler term of geopolitics.

Out of these backgrounds, Professor Karl Haushofer at Munich developed the Institut für Geopolitik, which made elaborate studies of the political geography of the world and formulated dynamic plans for action by which Germany might achieve her place in the sun. This was not an objective study but rather a tool of military imperialism and a means of propaganda. Under his direction the ideas of *lebensraum* and Heartland were extended far beyond their original concept.

Haushofer gave relatively little attention to the New World and, since military advance westward against France and Britain appeared difficult, the natural direction of German expansion was thought to lie in the east, toward and into the Soviet Union. Many of these ideas are echoed in Adolf Hitler's "Mein Kampf." Haushofer recognized the importance of Mackinder's work and saw the strategic significance of the Heartland as the key to German security. This area behind mountains and deserts was immune to sea-launched attack from Britain and might furnish a secure production base in a program of world conquest. Only through the effort of advanced European technique and capital could it be developed.

The German program was thus directed to acquisition of the intervening states and of Soviet territory. Haushofer also recognized that one who attacks a country of such broad

[1] *Ibid.*, 611.
[2] Lin Yu-tang, Geopolitics: Law of the Jungle, *Asia*, LXIII (1943), 200.

spaces has to win a decisive victory rather than merely to drive the enemy farther and farther back until the area that is sought is occupied. Space is an effective weapon of defense. Neither Haushofer nor any other German advocated a consistent policy toward the Soviet Union, nor did they commit themselves as to how the political consolidation of eastern Europe and the Heartland was to be brought about. The popularization of geopolitics was largely in terms of arousing the German people to their supposed destiny and of preparing the way for military or other conquest.

It was to prevent Germany's access to the Soviet Union that Mackinder had advocated a tier of independent buffer states between the two countries. We now see that this zone did not prove adequate, for Hitler was able to break down the corridor of nations such as Poland and Czechoslovakia and thus acquire direct access to the Soviet frontier. The basic concerns of Mackinder still remain: How can we isolate the Teuton and the Slav? How can we guarantee that Germany and the Soviet Union will not unite at some future date?

Soviet geographers have given little attention to geopolitics or to the geographic aspects of German ideas of *lebensraum* and Heartland. Instead they have regarded them merely as parts of the fascist system, distinct from the science of political geography.

The Russian historian V. O. Kluchevsky has written a monumental history of the Russian state from a strictly geopolitical point of view. In it he evaluates the geographic and ethnographic factors that influenced the territorial and political evolution of the principality of Moscow into the final expanse of the czarist empire. Kluchevsky maintains that the early Slavs started their long course of emigration eastward because of geographic and social forces that did not operate among the Germanic peoples who were the inheritors of the earlier Roman civilization. The eastern Slavs, on the contrary, living in boundless and inhospitable plains, found no fixed centers of habitation and thus were led to a seminomadic and warlike life. This environmental factor, states Kluchevsky, is the essential key to the understanding of Russian history. In this continental environment the Russians have pushed their frontiers outward in all directions until blocked by the sea to the north and east, or by mountains and deserts in the south, or by powerful states to the west.

GEOSTRATEGY FOR THE U.S.S.R.

Geography is equally important in the international relations of peace and war, for it involves not only physical location but accessibility and the many cultural and environmental qualities that make some places more desirable than others. These are active factors and as such bring consequences, planned or otherwise. They inescapably affect the policy of nations.

Strategy is defined as the application of policy and, in its geographic phases, calls for a recognition of the significance of place and all that goes with it. These practical aspects of political geography are sometimes known as geopolitics but, since "geography in action" covers much more than government and the term is often misunderstood because of its German connotations, it seems better to use the word geostrategy for the dynamic aspects of applied international geography. Political geography, as such, functions largely in the field of description and analysis. Geostrategy, on the other hand, is active and deals with forces and results. The fact that German writers have perverted Geopolitik into an imperialistic tool does not invalidate objective attempts to appraise international relations in geographic terms.

Geographic strategy involves the interrelationship of at

least ten elements: (1) size, (2) shape, (3) accessibility, (4) location, (5) boundaries, (6) relation to the ocean, (7) topography, (8) natural resources, (9) climate, and (10) people. The following paragraphs will evaluate these in turn and examine the validity of the Heartland concept as applied to the U.S.S.R. It will appear that the disadvantages outweigh the seeming advantages.

1. The importance of size was dramatically demonstrated during the Second World War when great value was placed upon defense in depth. The Soviet Union and China were able to retreat in the face of the enemy and thereby sell space with which to buy time for further resistance. In contrast, Belgium and Holland were defeated from the air within a few days; no type of government or degree of loyalty could have made up for their small size.

In 1943 Mackinder, defending his original statements, said, ". . . In its [the Russian Army's] rear is the vast plain of the Heartland, available for defense in depth and for strategic retreat. Away back this plain recedes eastward into natural bulwarks constituted by the 'inaccessible' Arctic Coast, the Lenaland wilderness behind the Yenisei and the fringe of mountains from the Altai to the Hindu Kush, backed by the Gobi, Tibetan, and Iranian deserts. These three barriers have breadth and substance, and far excel in defensive value the coasts and mountains which engird France." [1]

But mere size is not enough. No large army could withdraw into Middle Asia or northern Siberia and survive, for the productive facilities are entirely inadequate. Too great an area may be a handicap unless united by adequate communications. The Heartland is large and remote, but it is

---

[1] MACKINDER, HALFORD J., The Round World and the Winning of the Peace, *Foreign Affairs*, XXI (1943), 599.

devoid of the essential material possibilities for major economic strength.

No country anywhere will have sufficient size to be immune to air attack tomorrow or to furnish an adequate base for world conquest. Nor could a combination of neighboring nations, such as the Soviet Union and China, or the Soviet Union and Germany, be secure on the basis of size alone. Mackinder overlooked the fact that his Heartland is just over the top of the world from North America. With the air age, there are no longer any inaccessible countries or continental cores. The apparent inaccessibility of interior Asia as seen on a Mercator map by naval-minded eyes becomes quite different when viewed on a polar projection in terms of aviation.

2. Form or shape is a second element in geostrategy. A nation like Chile is so drawn out that while her area equals that of Germany, economic unity is made difficult. Canada appears compact on the map, but her population is as attenuated as that of Chile, no more than a fringe along the boundary of the United States. Whereas Mackinder's Heartland is compact with a satisfactory gross shape, the distribution of good land and people and communications within it is so eccentric that the form lacks coherence. Millions of square miles are eliminated from normal settlement because of too short a growing season or too little rainfall. Vast areas have almost no people, or any possibility of industrial production or trade. Much of interior and northern Eurasia has little prospective value, for it is either bleak Arctic tundra, stunted forest, or desert. The utilizable section is in the thin end of the triangle of settlement. The value of the Heartland is lessened by its empty areas which break it up into isolated fragments and destroy its coherent shape.

3. Accessibility is of great importance in economic geography. Anything beyond subsistence livelihood requires trade

and communications. Areas are not usable unless they are get-at-able. Deserts, mountains, and trackless forests bar access to millions of square miles in the Heartland. The western part of the Soviet Union is well supplied with a network of railways, but interior Asia is nearly inaccessible in terms of modern communications. Great areas are many tens of miles from railways, navigable rivers, or automobile roads. Elsewhere travel is by carts, camels, or pack animals. Northern Siberia has only its rivers, ice-bound for six to nine months of the year. The coherence and invulnerability of a Heartland need to be considered in terms of internal accessibility as well as its external approaches.

The Soviet Union is influenced by its position in the most isolated part of Asia and the climatically least desirable portion of Europe. The country borders the frozen Arctic Ocean as well as the semifrozen North Pacific for many miles, but it is almost isolated from the open Atlantic. This disadvantageous position would be even more of a handicap were not the Union's economy so largely self-sufficient.

The Soviet state lies along one of the frontiers of the inhabited earth, isolated from maritime contacts on its long northern coast line by perennial ice and elsewhere, except in the west, by mountains and deserts. The Arctic shore is no longer inaccessible in the absolute sense of a few years ago. Merchant ships, with the help of powerful icebreakers and reconnaissance air flights, regularly trade to the Ob, Yenisei, and Lena rivers, but a military invasion across the vast ice pack and over the tundra mosses and taiga forests of northern Siberia seems almost impossible. The approaches to Soviet territory on the south are scarcely less formidable, for deserts and rugged mountains bar access. No railroad leads to Iran, Afghanistan, or India, and the one line to China is merely a short cut to the Soviet Pacific rather than an avenue of trade to China. A new trans-Asian railway via Sinkiang and Middle Asia will alter this in part, but the unproductive desert and the distance will remain.

The Heartland may have citadel-like inaccessibility, but poor communications are not only a barrier to invasion; they are equally a handicap for peacetime trade and internal development.

4. Location is the prime question in all geography; not "where" in terms of latitude and longitude, but "where" in terms of good land and markets and world highways. The Heartland represents the climax of continentality, but few nations have achieved cultural or any other progress without external stimulus. Cultural progress results from contacts, as opposed to isolation. Hence an area that provides intercourse tends to develop progress. China may have wished that she did not have such an exposed coast line, but the peacetime assets greatly outweigh the military liabilities. Japan has an excellent insular position in the western Pacific but lacks a secure home base. Her defeat became so difficult during the Second World War because of her newly enlarged size and her central position within this temporary empire.

The significance of location can change. Thus Rome was once the center of the civilized world but the Mediterranean is now a minor body of water. Interior Asia is increasing its population, but there is no likelihood that it will ever hold the controlling part of mankind. Nor is it likely that a developed Heartland could be controlled by a Germany or any other alien power far from the center of gravity. We of the twentieth century live in a world dominated by the North Atlantic rather than by a continental interior.

5. Boundaries frequently present problems: here is the fifth component of geostrategy. Mackinder has followed deserts and mountains in defining the Heartland. These form natural obstacles to ground travel but not to the air-

plane. If such barriers keep armies from trespassing, they equally keep out goods, people, and ideas. One may question whether there can any longer be any effective frontiers with the development of radio and the airplane.

6. The ocean is still the cheapest highway; without free access to it, a nation suffers. The history of civilization may be traced in terms of progressively larger and larger water bodies, from the Nile to the Aegean, and in turn to the Mediterranean and Atlantic, and in some measure in the future to the Pacific. Oceans are highways, not barriers; they unite peoples rather than isolate them. The Heartland has a long border next to the Arctic Ocean, but this is useless for much of the year.

The history of Russia may be written in terms of its search for ocean ports. The Russian Bear will not be content until it finds warm water, and this is equally true regardless of whether the government be a czarist autarchy or Soviet socialism. Thus Peter is known as "the Great" because he gave Russia a window to Europe in St. Petersburg. Subsequent conquests under Catherine II provided access to the Black Sea, but this route to the ocean may easily be blocked at Constantinople, Gibraltar, and Suez. Pressure against Persia has continued for more than a century, partly with the hope of securing a port on the Persian Gulf. Since this would at once threaten Britain's life line to India, the Kremlin and Number Ten Downing Street have repeatedly been in conflict. Intrigues in Afghanistan, Tibet, Mongolia, Manchuria, and elsewhere in China are parts of the same inescapable program. Late in the nineteenth century the Trans-Siberian Railway was built as another attempt to get at the open sea. The extension of Russian interests to Port Arthur then produced the war with Japan in 1904-1905. Soviet foreign policy may be expected to have freer access to the ocean as one of its permanent ambitions.

7. Topography is the seventh element in geostrategy. Here Eurasia suffers, for rugged ranges isolate its various realms. The Himalaya assuredly provide the Heartland with security from invasion on the south, but they also block trade. Within the U.S.S.R. there are few topographic barriers that bar internal communications. But while land forms are favorable, Arctic swamps and frozen ground are handicaps. Even the rivers in the U.S.S.R. flow in the wrong direction, since the Lena, Yenisei, and Ob empty into the frozen Arctic and the Volga into the land-locked Caspian.

8. Natural resources, both mineral and agricultural, are vital in our modern world. Other nations in other times have achieved conspicuous success in art or philosophy, but in the twentieth century national greatness rests, perhaps too much, on coal, oil, iron, copper, aluminum, and sulphur. Lord Curzon remarked that, during the First World War, the Allies "floated to victory on a sea of oil." It should be added that during the Second World War they flew to victory on a cloud of gasoline.

Nature has unfortunately played favorites and has distributed the good things of the earth unevenly. It is now clear that the Union is one of the richest countries on earth, but no nation is fully self-sufficient. Soviet coal, oil, iron, gold, potassium salts, and phosphate are of vast extent. Not all her mineral deposits are of high grade, however, nor are they all easily accessible or near the requisite fuel. Although the major picture is one of exceptional abundance, overoptimistic conclusions should not be drawn for a mere tabulation. It does not appear that interior Eurasia will ever lead the world in industry, and decades must elapse before this area will exploit its more obvious resources and reach the level of material culture of the Atlantic world. International trade remains inevitable.

The Union has some of the finest agricultural soils in the

world, but unfortunately they are located in a region of variable rainfall and drought. The agricultural area cannot be pushed much beyond its present boundaries, and it is well to remember that Soviet possibilities more nearly resemble those of Canada than of the United States. Forest resources are abundant.

9. Climate is next to the last but far from the least of these factors. Health and progress are directly related to it. It is not likely that a League of Nations will ever have its capital in Moscow or in Yakutsk. Nor will exceptionally healthy people live in these areas. Maps of climatic energy give lower rank to most of Asia than to Europe or North America. The long period of winter inactivity in the Heartland is certainly a disadvantage. Agriculture is as vitally affected by climate as is man. Drought and frost are continual hazards, the former along the southern frontier of agriculture and the latter toward the north.

10. People are of inescapable geographic importance. Who lives here, what is their cultural background, what are their ideals and objectives, and how numerous are they? Within the U.S.S.R. are 200,000,000 people, but about half of them live west of the Volga and so outside Mackinder's Heartland. The nine million square miles of this area have an average density of but 15 per square mile, with vast areas that are essentially empty. These numbers will increase but the population-supporting capacity is low. It does not seem likely that the inhabitants of interior Asia will ever be of first rank in world importance.

On the other hand, the Soviet people have developed conspicuous patriotism and unity and have been welded together by the pioneering tasks of the five-year programs. Whether or not this is a Heartland characteristic is another matter. Mackinder seems to have given too little weight to this problem.

This analysis of the components of geostrategy is directed to a consideration of the Heartland, but it also serves as a check list for the detailed consideration of each region described in the preceding chapters. No deterministic approach is possible, for human factors may reverse the totality of the physical environment. Thus language, nationality, religion, population density, and occupations are each of geographic concern. Mere size is not a country's most important geographic character. The human drama is always more challenging than the material.

The function of geostrategy is to understand a nation's problems and potential, and to suggest a program of internal development and international cooperation that will be of mutual value. And if wars are to recur, it may indicate the wisest course of action in emergency. This is nothing more than applied geography.

In place of the Heartland concept, it would appear more in line with geographic realities to suggest that the interior cores of continents will remain of lesser importance and that the important areas of Eurasia will be peripheral. The U.S.S.R. is not the same as the Heartland, for as a nation it has outlets to the Pacific and is in contact with Europe and the Atlantic world. Peace and prosperity lie not in withdrawal into the interior but in active cooperation in a world society.

If there is anywhere a world citadel or Heartland, it may well lie in North America rather than in Eurasia. The American continent has adequate size, compact shape, internal accessibility, a central location, good boundaries, access to two oceans, favorable topography, rich minerals, excellent climate, and a dynamic spirit in its people. Twice in the twentieth century it has been demonstrated that no war can be won without the aid of the United States. Just as there are no wars but world wars, and no world wars but total wars, so we must learn that there is no peace but world peace, and no world peace but total peace.

These are the assets of national strength today: intelligent and loyal people, technological skill, industry and organization, adequate size and secure location, natural resources, and able government. Nowhere are these more adequate than in North America. The Soviet Union has many of them but not all, for industry is immature and much of its area is as yet unexploited. Its citizens are loyal but still below the cultural level of western Europe. China offers certain potentials; so may India and Brazil; but they are not found elsewhere.

AMERICAN RELATIONS WITH THE SOVIET UNION [1]

At the conclusion of the Second World War the bulk of the world's military and industrial might will be in the hands of the United States and the Soviet Union. Whether this new situation will hold seeds of catastrophe or of opportunity will be determined by policies still to be formulated. If this concentration of power leads to a struggle for supremacy, tragedy will follow. If it is used cooperatively to maintain order, then the stage is set for an era of prosperity and peace. This will depend upon good will and intelligence.

The people of the United States can no longer afford to allow their relations with the Soviets to be guided by prejudice, whether of the Left or the Right. Industry must make it its business to be informed; so too must the politician and the ordinary citizen.

Without such an understanding there can be no reason-

[1] The author is indebted to James H. McGraw, Jr., for permission to use some of the following ideas from an article of his published in the *New York Herald Tribune* in October, 1944. His material has here been considerably altered and does not necessarily represent Mr. McGraw's ideas as originally presented.

able hope for reduction of our tax burden. If the threat of a clash between these two giants impends, neither bankers nor governments will run the risk of lending on a scale adequate to maintain international trade at levels necessary for our future prosperity. Most potential international customers, instead of buying freely in open world markets, will be forced, as during the dangerous period introduced by Hitler in the early 1930's, into the trading camp of whichever power they fear most.

During the years since it was attacked by Hitler, the Soviet Union has conclusively proved to a doubting world that it is a top-flight military and economic power.

Soviet railroads did not break down under the strain of war. Regions accounting for nearly 70 per cent of the key industries were engulfed by the invading Nazis but, before they fell, Soviet engineers performed a near miracle by transplanting entire industries a thousand miles to the Urals with the loss of as little as four months' production in many cases.

Though American planes, trucks, and medical supplies were welcomed by Moscow, fairness demands the admission that the great bulk of Soviet military supplies was produced within their own country by their own tools. It was Russian planning and Russian equipment that won the victories of Leningrad, Stalingrad, and Moscow.

But these measures of Soviet military strength, indicative as they are of an unsuspected economic development and national unity, fail to picture in adequate detail the potential of the Soviet developments after the war.

The population of the Union numbers 200,000,000 and is increasing at the rate of 2,800,000 a year. Furthermore, the country has three times as many young people under sixteen years of age as has the United States. This is a measure both of war potential and of vast productive capacity. Probably in no other part of the world before the war was per capita production rising as rapidly as in the Soviet Union.

German armies occupied a region roughly equivalent to territory in the United States north of Virginia and east of the Mississippi. This huge area, with its counterparts of Pittsburgh, Buffalo, and Bridgeport; of Illinois cornfields, New York dairy farms, and Maine potato lands, was twice subjected to the most withering destruction: first by the Russians themselves when they retreated before the Germans and then by the Germans when they withdrew before the victorious Russians.

As a result, this area and these people are in need of complete reoutfitting. They need houses and shoes, trolley cars and baby carriages, tractors and livestock, hydroelectric plants and electric-light bulbs. Most of these needs will be met at home. But for the rebuilding and expansion of her industries the Soviet Union looks to the United States for basic equipment.

It is important to remember that the bulk of the Soviet's iron and steel industry, its nonferrous mining and processing, some of its chemical production, much of its coke roasting and gas recovery, practically its entire automobile and tractor industry, and the largest of its hydroelectric plants are based on American machinery and processes. Many of the largest projects under the first five-year plans were designed, built, and operated by American firms. The Soviets are now seeking bids on new shipbuilding equipment, construction and road-building machinery, alloy steels, textile machines, plastics, and a long list of rail, air, and water transport supplies.

In the opinion of E. C. Ropes, chief of the Russian unit of the Bureau of Foreign and Domestic Commerce,[1] the

[1] Ropes, E. C., The Soviet Union in World Trade, *World Economics*, published by Institute of World Economics (1944).

first category of needs from the United States includes equipment for the electrical industry, coal-mining machinery and other types of mining equipment, automobile and tractor machinery, and plants for chemical industries including synthetic rubber and plastics. In a second group Mr. Ropes places transportation equipment for railroads and aviation, radio and telephone supplies, highway machinery, refrigeration equipment, and facilities for meat packing and canning.

The Soviet Union, however, has more than a rehabilitation job on its drawing boards. The First Five-year Plan, which was completed ahead of time in 1932, was devoted almost exclusively to heavy industry. The Union set out to build for itself the machines and the factories which, in later years, could manufacture at home the modern equipment for a vast range of light industries. It was hoped that, by the end of the Second Five-year Plan, Soviet factories would begin to turn out a flow of consumer goods: ready-made dresses, canned foods, soap, cosmetics, shoes, kitchenware, automobiles, telephones, and modern houses.

But, by 1935, Moscow realized that the Union could not afford to enjoy such luxuries in the face of growing political tension in Europe. So, when the Third Five-year Plan was launched, there was no fanfare. Russians continued to wear their old clothes, to eat whatever simple food was available, and began grimly to build the industries that ultimately produced enough tanks, planes, and guns to turn the tide of battle at Stalingrad. It is characteristic of Moscow that, even before the last battles with the Nazis are over, the Russians are planning to pick up their plans for industrial expansion where the war interrupted them.

Soviet officials propose to establish a permanent exhibition of American goods in Moscow so that their public will see samples of new machine tools, aluminum and alloy products, oil-drilling machinery, bulldozers, and prefabricated kitchen equipment. Russia already is projecting specific plans to resume the job (1) of making the country an industrial giant comparable to the United States and (2) of making life more pleasant for a long-suffering people.

What is the measure of this postwar market in the Soviet Union? Some estimates place the total quantity of goods which the U.S.S.R. might take from the United States during the first two or three years after the war as high as $5,000,000,000 a year. Such estimates are probably far too optimistic, even if the United States were prepared to help the Soviets pay by buying vast quantities of raw materials and to provide large credits to handle the purchases during the first few years of rehabilitation. The Soviet Union will certainly produce just as much of her own needs as possible and will end any unbalanced foreign trade at the earliest possible moment, but she is so anxious to industrialize that she will be willing to accept the necessary imports under any appropriate terms in order to get under way again.

The relations of American exporters with the Soviet Union during the period covered by the three five-year plans have been eminently satisfactory. Moscow has met all its obligations punctually; fifteen years of experience have reduced contract forms to the point where they cause a minimum of misunderstanding between the Russian representatives and the American producers; and individual American companies with extensive prewar experience in handling Soviet business are offering large credits on initial postwar orders.

But the volume of trade after the war hinges upon Moscow's ability to pay and American willingness to buy. Never before the war did the United States buy more than $30,000,000 of goods a year from the Soviet Union. As late as 1938, Soviet exports to this country amounted to as little as $23,500,000—far less than enough to pay even the service charges on the credits that would have to be extended in connection with exports of several billion dollars a year. Only South Africa produces more new gold each year than the Soviet Union. But the United States does not want gold; more of it would only complicate the problem of controlling prices here.

Unless the United States can absorb far more of the kinds of goods bought from Russia before the war—furs, timber, manganese, chromium, and handicrafts—or can find important new imports, credits of the size necessary to fill immediate Soviet needs could not be serviced without large supplemental importations of undesirable gold. Additional import trade may be developed in anthracite coal from the Donets Basin, fish, caviar, and crab meat, pulpwood from the northern forests, and petroleum from Baku.

The nub of the situation is that the U.S.S.R. offers a large potential market, particularly for American heavy industries. If this sales outlet is to materialize, then the United States must find a way to import from the Union from ten to twenty times as much as she did before the war. Instead of merely going after the export business, American businessmen must explore with the Russians the possibility of buying bigger supplies of Soviet products. The United States cannot expect to sell unless she is willing to buy; the volume of her possible exports is conditioned by the volume of her imports.

Much more than this Soviet market itself hinges upon sound cooperative action by the world's two leading military-industrial nations. If trade between them is held to a minimum and if relations are strained, the flow of trade all over the world will be adversely affected. And any refusal of the Soviet Union and the United States to work cooperatively to maintain the peace would kill all dreams of a vast industrialization program for China.

Geostrategy and the Future of the Union

The opportunity to make a conspicuous change in the cultural map of the world, and at the same time to achieve better political understanding, is before us. It demands of Americans intelligence and imagination. It demands realistic action by recognition of the fact that the solution to America's foreign-trade problem lies in boosting imports as well as exports. We can sell no more than we are willing to buy. Friendship thrives best with healthy economic relations, and these grow in an atmosphere of understanding.

Two things are clear. The first lesson of geography is interdependence, and the first requirement of world citizenship is an understanding of global geography.

SUGGESTED READINGS

1. ONE-SIXTH OF THE EARTH

General References on the Soviet Union

The preparation of these chapters involved an extensive bibliography in Russian but, since the material is not easily available, the following notations are largely limited to references in English.

The newest volume on Soviet geography is "The U.S.S.R., a Geographical Survey," by JAMES S. GREGORY and D. W. SHAVE, London: Harrap (1944). Another recent volume is "The Land of the Russian People," by ALEXANDER NAZAROFF, Philadelphia and New York: Lippincott (1944).

Few geographic texts on Europe or Asia give adequate attention to the U.S.S.R. Two thoughtful chapters are in SAMUEL VAN VALKENBURG and ELLS-WORTH HUNTINGTON: "Europe," New York: Wiley (1935); and a somewhat longer treatment may be found in GEORGE D. HUBBARD: "Geography of Europe," New York: Appleton-Century (1937). An excellent analysis is that by P. CAMENA D'ALMEIDA: "Etats de la Baltique, Russie" (1932), in the French series entitled "Géographie universelle." A similar survey is provided in four sections of the "Klute Handbuch." In "Mitteleuropa, Osteuropa," Potsdam (1933), are articles by MAX FRIEDERICHSEN: Das Europäische Russland, 321-434; and BRUNO PLAETSCHKE: Die Kaukasusländer, 435-464. The volume "Nordasien, Zentral-und Ostasien," Potsdam (1937), contains HEL-MUT ANGER: Siberien, 125-210; and ARVED SCHULTZ: Russisch Turkestan, 211-244.

The best geographical material from the Soviet viewpoint is in the volumes by NICHOLAS MIKHAILOV entitled "Soviet Geography," London: Methuen (1935); and "Land of the Soviets," New York: Furman (1939). Geographic ideology is presented in a chapter by VLADIMIR ROMM entitled Geographic Tendencies in the Soviet Union, in SAMUEL N. HARPER: "The Soviet Union and World-problems," Chicago: University Press (1935). There is a short but very worth-while article with maps by BENJAMIN SEMENOV-TIAN-SHANSKY: Russia: Territory and Population, *Geographical Review*, XVII (1928), 616-640. See, also, R. M. FLEMING, An Outline of Some Factors in the Development of Russia, in "Studies in Regional Consciousness and Environment," New York: Oxford University Press.

Unsurpassed cartographic information dealing with all aspects of geography is available in the first and second volumes of the "Great Soviet World Atlas," Moscow (1938 and 1940), with a translation volume by GEORGE B. CRESSEY. A convenient reference for place names is the LITERARY DIGEST "Map of the U.S.S.R.," New York: Funk (1934). Current Russian literature and maps may be obtained from the Four Continent Book Corporation, 255

Suggested Readings

Fifth Avenue, New York City. The AMERICAN RUSSIAN INSTITUTE, 58 Park Ave., New York 19, published a useful map in 1942 which indicates changes in place names together with new industrial developments. Two small convenient atlases of economic information with supplementary text are "Soviet Russia in Maps," Chicago: Denoyer-Geppert (1942); and JASPER H. STEMBRIDGE: "An Atlas of the U.S.S.R.," New York: Oxford University Press (1942). The newest and best map is the "Map of the Union of Soviet Socialist Republics," issued by the National Geographical Society in 1944, with an index.

Among the many histories of Russia, one of the best is D. S. MIRSKY: "Russia, A Social History," New York: Appleton-Century (1932). Interwar boundary changes are described by J. A. MORRISON: Territorial-administrative Structure of the U.S.S.R., *American Quarterly on the Soviet Union*, I (1938), 25-58. The quest of the Russian Bear for warm water is described in ROBERT J. KERNER: "The Urge to the Sea: The Course of Russian History," Berkeley: University of California Press (1942). An authoritative history is V. O. KLUCHEVSKY: "History of the Russian State," in 5 volumes, English translation by Hogart, New York: Dutton (1927-1931).

A comprehensive review is provided by P. MELEVSKY-MALEVITCH: "Russia U.S.S.R.," New York: W. F. Payson (1933). KARL BAEDEKER's "Russia," Leipzig: Baedeker (1914), is old but indispensable for detailed travel information. Current information is available from the AMERICAN RUSSIAN INSTITUTE, particularly their publication entitled *The American Review on the Soviet Union*. Economic data may be obtained from the RUSSIAN ECONOMIC INSTITUTE, 90 Morningside Drive, New York 27.

2. THE PATTERN OF EURASIA

The Geographical Personality

The most recent volume on the geography of Asia is GEORGE B. CRESSEY: "Asia's Lands and Peoples," New York: McGraw-Hill (1944). Only one other volume has been written by an American, namely, DANIEL R. BERGSMARK: "Economic Geography of Asia," New York: Prentice-Hall (1935).

British geographers have written two standard volumes on Asia: L. DUDLEY STAMP: "Asia," New York: Dutton, 3d ed. (1935); and LIONEL W. LYDE: "The Continent of Asia," London: Macmillan (1933). The outstanding French volumes are those in the series entitled "Géographie universelle," Paris: Librairie Armand Colin (1928-1932), with the following volumes devoted to parts of Asia: "Asie occidentale" by RAOUL BLANCHARD; "Haute Asie" by FERNAND GRENARD; "Asie des moussons" by JULES SION, Part 1, "Généralités—Chine—Japon"; Part 2, "Inde—Indochine—Insulinde"; and "Etats de la Baltique, Russie" by P. CAMENA D'ALMEIDA. The chief German series is in the "Klute Handbuch der Geographischen Wissenschaft," Potsdam Akademische Verlagsgesellschaft Athenaion (1931-1937), with two volumes entitled "Nordasien, Zentral-und Ostasien" and "Vorder-und Sudasien." A volume in Russian which deals with Asia outside the U.S.S.R. is V. M. STEIN: "Economic Geography of Asia," Leningrad: Geographic-Economic Scientific Research

Institute (1940), reviewed by GEORGE B. CRESSEY in the *Far Eastern Quarterly*, I (1942), 180-184. Two volumes, old but still useful, are A. H. KEANE: "Asia," London: Stanford (1906), 2 vols. For an anthropological survey see L. H. D. BUXTON: "The Peoples of Asia," New York: Knopf (1925). The geology is described by KURL LEUCHS: "Geologie von Asien," Berlin: Borntraeger (1937), 2 vols.

The Divisions of Eurasia

The classic account of Asiatic geology is that of EDUARD SUESS: "The Face of the Earth," Oxford: Clarendon Press (1904-1924), 5 vols.; summarized by J. W. GREGORY: Suess's Classification of Eurasian Mountains, *Geographical Journal*, XLV (1915), 497-513. A summary volume dealing with various parts of the continent is edited by J. W. GREGORY: "The Structure of Asia," London: Methuen (1929).

Climate and Vegetation

The best descriptions of regional climates are those by various authors in the "Koeppen-Geiger Handbuch der Klimatologie," Berlin: Borntraeger (1931). Somewhat older descriptions may be found in W. G. KENDREW: "The Climates of the Continents," Oxford: Clarendon Press (1927). Meteorological data are available in H. HELM CLAYTON: "World Weather Records," Smithsonian Miscellaneous Collections, LXXIX (1927) and XV (1934).

3. THE SOVIET PEOPLE

"The Peoples of the Soviet Union" by ALĚS HRDLIČKA, Washington: Smithsonian Institution (1942), is extensively quoted in Chap. 3. Some of the material in MIKHAILOV's "Soviet Geography" deals with human problems. HELEN PRATT has a volume on cultural history entitled "Russia from Tsarist Empire to Socialism," New York: Institute of Pacific Relations (1937). Interesting material is included in "The Russians," by ALBERT RHYS WILLIAMS, New York: Harcourt (1943); "Peoples of the U.S.S.R.," by ANNA LOUISE STRONG, New York: Macmillan (1944); "People on Our Side," by EDGAR SNOW, New York: Random House (1944); and EDDY GILMORE's I Learn about the Russians, *National Geographic Magazine*, LXXXIV (1943), 619-640. VLADIMIR JOCHELSON's "Peoples of Asiatic Russia," New York: American Museum of Natural History (1928), is old but valuable for cultural traits.

4. THE PHYSICAL FOUNDATION

The best reference in Russian on environmental conditions is L. S. BERG: "Priroda S.S.S.R." (The Natural Regions of the U.S.S.R.), Moscow and Leningrad (1937). Among PROFESSOR BERG's other volumes is one entitled "Geographical Zones of the U.S.S.R., Part I, Introduction, Tundra, The Forest

Suggested Readings

Zone," Leningrad (1930). There is a vast amount of comprehensive material in the series entitled "Reference Books on the Water Resources of the U.S.S.R.," issued for various regions by the HYDROLOGICAL SERVICE since 1936.

The Geological Base

The extensive literature on Soviet geology is well summarized in the various guidebooks, reports, and other publications of the SEVENTEENTH INTERNATIONAL GEOLOGICAL CONGRESS, Moscow (1937); especially in the article by A. D. ARKHANGUELSKY: Structure géologique et histoire géologique de l'URSS in Vol. II of the *Report*, 285-304. ARKHANGUELSKY has also written a guidebook for the Second International Congress of Soil Science, Moscow (1930), entitled "Outline of the Structure and History of the Russian Platform." V. A. OBRUCHEV: "Geology of Siberia" is available in a German edition (1926) and in Russian (1935-1936). The first volume of KURT LEUCHS: "Géologie von Asien" is devoted to Northern Asia. The best summary of glaciation is I. P. GERASIMOV and K. K. MARKOV: "The Glacial Period in the Territory of the U.S.S.R.," (in Russian with a 20-page English summary); see review in *Geographical Review*, XXXI (1941), 343-345; and RICHARD FOSTER FLINT and HERBERT G. DORSEY, JR.: Glaciation in Siberia, *Bulletin* Geological Society of America, LVI (1945), 89-106. Permanently frozen ground is described in GEORGE B. CRESSEY: Frozen Ground in Siberia, *Journal of Geology*, XLVII (1939), 472-488. Volumes II and III of "The Face of the Earth" by EDUARD SUESS contain old but significant comments on Russia.

Land Form Regions

Only scattered material is available on regional geomorphology, but the following articles clear up the structure of northeastern Siberia: S. V. OBRUCHEV and K. A. SALISHCHEV: The Mountain Systems of Northeastern Asia, *Geographical Review*, XXV (1935), 625-642; and V. A. OBRUCHEV: The Yablonovi and Stanovoi Ranges in the Light of New Data, *Geographical Journal*, LXXXVI (1935), 422-440. The most authoritative statement in Russian is by B. TH. DOBRYNIN: Geomorphological Divisions of European U.S.S.R., presented to the International Geographical Congress, Warsaw (1934).

Climatic Characteristics

The most detailed climatic study is A. V. VOZNESENSKY: "Map of the Climates of the U.S.S.R.," (in Russian with English summary), Leningrad: *Transactions* Bureau of Agro-Meteorology, XXI (1930). The section of the "Koeppen-Geiger Handbuch" on Klimakunde von Russland (in Europa und Asien) contains tables and a map of climatic regions. KENDREW's "Climates of the Continents" has a chapter on the Russian Empire. Two articles by STANISLAUS NOVAKOVSKY deal with the human climatology: The Effect of Climate on the Efficiency of the People of the Russian Far East, *Ecology*, III (1922), 275-283; and Arctic or Siberian Hysteria as a Reflex of the Geographic Environment, *Ecology*, V (1924), 113-127. A brief summary of the environment is in L. I. PRASOLOV: The Climate and Soils of Northern Eurasia as Conditions of Colonization, in "Pioneer Settlement" issued by the American Geographical Society, New York (1932), 240-260.

Natural Vegetation

WILLIAM SEIFRIZ has written a series of articles entitled Sketches of the Vegetation of Some Southern Provinces of Soviet Russia, in the *Journal of Ecology*, XIX (1931), 360-371, 372-382; XX (1932), 53-68, 69-77, 78-88; XXIII (1935), 140-146, 147-160. See also BORIS A. KELLER: Distribution of Vegetation on the Plains of Southern Russia, *Journal of Ecology*, XV (1927), 189-233. There is a good description of European forests in RAPHAEL ZON and W. N. SPARHAWK: "Forest Resources of the World," I, New York: McGraw-Hill (1923). Descriptions of dry-land forests may be found in G. N. VYSSOTSKY: Shelterbelts in the Steppes of Russia, *Journal of Forestry*, XXXIII (1935), 781-788; and N. T. MIROV: Two Centuries of Afforestation and Shelterbelt Planting on the Russian Steppes, *Journal of Forestry*, XXXIII (1935), 971-973.

Soils

"The Great Soil Groups of the World and Their Development" written in Russian by J. D. GLINKA has been translated by CURTIS F. MARBUT, Ann Arbor: Edwards Bros. (1927). Numerous articles on soils and related geographic problems were published in the *Proceedings* and *Guidebooks* of the Second International Congress of Soil Science. Moscow (1930).

5. SOVIET MINERAL WEALTH

Some of the best material is that issued in connection with the Seventeenth International Geological Congress, including an expected volume on "Petroleum Resources of the World." A bulletin prepared by M. M. PRIGOROVSKY is entitled "The Coal Resources of the U.S.S.R." Three of the delegates subsequently wrote of their observations: CYRIL FOX: Mineral Development in Soviet Russia, *Transactions* Mining, Geological, and Metallurgical Institute of India, XXXIV (1938), part 2, 100-201; E. L. BRUCE: Mineral Deposits of the Southern Ukraine and of the Ural Mountains, *Canadian Mining and Metallurgical Bulletin*, CCCXIX (1938), 505-523; and TOM EDWARDS: The Mineral Deposits of the U.S.S.R., *The Mining Magazine*, LVIII (1938), 265-279, 335-343.

The UNITED GEOLOGICAL AND PROSPECTING SERVICE OF THE U.S.S.R. issued two bulletins in 1933, Mineral Resources of the U.S.S.R., and Power Resources of the U.S.S.R. A comprehensive volume entitled "Electric Power Development in the U.S.S.R.," which includes both coal and water resources, was prepared by the KRZIZHANOVSKY POWER INSTITUTE of the Academy of Sciences in 1936.

The latest information on various products is available in *The Minerals Industry*, McGraw-Hill (annual). A recent publication is ANDREW J. STEIGER: "Wartime Changes in the Use of and Search for Soviet Natural Resources," in The American Russian Institute's; The U.S.S.R. in Reconstruction (1944),

111-125. A short evaluation will be found in G. W. TYRRELL: "The Development of Mineral Resources in the Soviet Union"; in JOSEPH NEEDHAM and JANE SYKES DAVIES: "Science in Soviet Russia," London: Watts (1942). There is an excellent series on lead and zinc in The Metalliferous Altai of Soviet Russia by ANDREW and EDITH MEYER in the *Engineering and Mining Journal,* CXXXVII (1936), 275-278, 348-353, 468-472, 476, 515-520. A comprehensive article on Russian aluminum is R. J. ANDERSON: Russian Aluminum, *The Mining Magazine,* LVIII (1938), 73-86. The UNITED STATES BUREAU OF MINES has prepared an article on Mineral Production and Trade of the U.S.S.R. (Russia), *Foreign Minerals Quarterly,* I, No. 2 (1938), 1-72. A comprehensive report now somewhat out of date is The Petroleum Resources of Russia by ARTHUR HUBER REDFIELD, *Bulletin* American Association of Petroleum Geologists, II (1927), 493-513.

6. INDUSTRIALIZATION IN THE SOVIET UNION

Interesting accounts of economic developments during the early five-year plans are contained in the volume by the former *Christian Science Monitor* correspondent, WILLIAM H. CHAMBERLIN: "Russia's Iron Age," Boston: Little (1934); the report of an engineer, ALCAN HIRSCH: "Industrialized Russia," New York: Reinhold (1934); and CALVIN B. HOOVER: "The Economic Life of Soviet Russia," New York: Macmillan (1931). Current developments are reported in the U. S. BUREAU OF FOREIGN COMMERCE, *Foreign Commerce Weekly* and its predecessor, *Russian Economic Notes.* The AMERICAN-RUSSIAN CHAMBER OF COMMERCE published a "Handbook of the Soviet Union" in 1935. WILLIAM MANDEL has written on Soviet Transport, Today and Tomorrow in *The American Review on the Soviet Union,* III (1941), 28-45.

Agriculture

Numerous maps of agricultural conditions are presented in the articles by OLOF JONASSON entitled Agricultural Regions of Europe, *Economic Geography,* I (1925), 277-314, and II (1926), 19-48. Specialized material on agriculture is contained in two publications by VLADIMIR P. TIMOSHENKO: "Agricultural Russia and the Wheat Problem," Stanford University: Food Research Institute (1932); and "Russia as a Producer and Exporter of Wheat," Stanford University: Food Research Institute (1932). Changes in farming are described by W. LADEJINSKY: Collectivization of Agriculture in the Soviet Union, *Political Science Quarterly,* XLIX (1934), 1-43, 207-252; and Soviet State Farms, *Political Science Quarterly,* LIII (1938), 60-82, 207-232. Critical conditions in the south are presented by N. M. TULAIKOV: Agriculture in the Dry Region of the U.S.S.R., *Economic Geography,* VI (1930), 54-80. CURTIS F. MARBUT, former Chief of the U. S. Bureau of Soils, has written two articles growing out of his visit to the Second International Soil Congress, Russia and the United States in the World's Wheat Market, *Geographical Review,* XXI (1931), 1-21; and Agriculture in the United States and Russia, *Geographical Review,* XXI (1931), 598-612. In this connection there is a valuable comment by V. P. TIMOSHENKO: The Expansion of the

Wheat Area in Arid Russia, *Geographical Review*, XXIII (1933), 479-481. Conditions in the late 1930's are described by LAZAR VOLIN: Recent Developments in Soviet Agriculture, *Foreign Agriculture*, I (1937), 3-28; Effects of the Drought and Purge on the Agriculture of the Soviet Union, III (1939), 175-196; The Russian Peasant Household under the Mir and the Collective Farm System, IV (1940), 133-146.

7. REGIONS OF SOVIET EUROPE

Regional references on Soviet Europe, which will not be repeated under the various regions, include MIKHAILOV, HUBBARD, D'ALMEIDA, and FRIEDERICHSEN. Another excellent source is L. S. BERG: "The Natural Regions of the U.S.S.R.," in Russian. BAEDEKER's "Russia" is invaluable for city maps and travel information. Excursion guidebooks for the Seventeenth International Geological Congress deal with the Caucasus, the Urals, Kola-Karelia, Moscow, the petroleum areas, the Ukraine and Crimea, Nova Zemlya, and Siberia.

Ukrainia

Farming conditions are described in LOUIS G. MICHAEL: The Soviet Ukraine—Its People and Agriculture, *Foreign Agriculture*, III (1939), 281-306. Two articles on mineral wealth are those by STANISLAUS NOVAKOVSKI: Natural Resources of Ukraine, *Journal of Geography*, XXIII (1924), 293-300; and E. L. BRUCE: Mineral Deposits of the Southern Ukraine and of the Ural Mountains, *Canadian Mining and Metallurgical Bulletin*, CCCXIX (1938), 505-523. Historical and political aspects are provided in "The Ukraine" by W. E. D. ALLEN, Cambridge: University Press (1940); and in A. S. ELWELL-SUTTON: The Ukraine, *Contemporary Review*, CLV (1939), 681-690. The character of the areas acquired in 1940 is considered in LOUIS ARNER BOYD's "Polish Countrysides," New York: American Geographical Society (1937). See also EDDY GILMORE: Liberated Ukraine, *National Geographic Magazine*, LXXXV (1944), 513-536.

The Baltic States

Interesting travel experiences are found in the *National Geographic Magazine*, LXXVI (1939), Estonia: At Russia's Baltic Gate by BARONESS IRINA UNGERN-STERNBERG, 803-834; Flying Around the Baltic by DOUGLAS CHANDLER, LXXIII (1938), 767-806; and Latvia, Home of the Letts by MAYNARD OWEN WILLIAMS, XLVI (1924), 401-443. MRS. ETHEL WOODS has prepared a study in physical and human geography, "The Baltic Region," New York: Dutton (1932). Commercial aspects are dealt with in an article by W. O. BLANCHARD: The Baltic Sea, *Journal of Geography*, XLIII (1944), 62-70.

Metropolitan Leningrad

EDMUND WILSON has written As I Saw Leningrad, *Travel*, LXVII (1936), 20-23, 60-61.

Suggested Readings

Kola-Karelian Taiga

Conditions of vegetation are considered by WILLIAM SEIFRIZ: The Plant Life of Russian Lapland, *Ecology*, XV (1934), 306-318; and R. RUGGLES GATES: Notes on the Tundra of Russian Lapland, *Journal of Ecology*, XVI (1928), 150-160. The exploitation of the potash deposits is described in the small volume by A. E. FERSMAN: "The Scientific Study of Soviet Mineral Resources," Moscow (1935). Economic developments are considered by WILLIAM O. FIELD, JR.: The Kola Peninsula, *American Quarterly on the Soviet Union*, I (1938), 3-21.

Dvina-Pechora Taiga

Forest and lumbering possibilities are dealt with by JOHN D. GUTHERIE: Some Notes on the Forests of Northern Russia, *Journal of Forestry*, XXII (1924), 197-204; and EDWARD P. STEBBING: The Forest Region of North East Russia and Its Importance to Great Britain, *Geographical Journal*, LI (1918), 359-374. An interesting account of travel from Leningrad to the Dvina River is DAVID R. BUXTON: A Journey in Northern Russia, *Blackwood's Magazine*, CCXXXIV (1933), 149-174.

Central Agricultural Region

M. MELVINA SVEC has written a travel account entitled Voyaging down the Volga, *Journal of Geography*, XXXVIII (1939), 297-304. For general surveys of the Volga see ST. KOLUPAILA and M. PARDE: La Volga, étude hydrologique, *Annales de géographie*, XLIII (1934), 32-48; and MAYNARD OWEN WILLIAMS: Mother Volga Defends Her Own, *National Geographic Magazine*, LXXXII (1942), 793-811.

Southern Agricultural Region

Problems in cultivating the steppe regions of the lower Volga are covered in N. M. TULAIKOV: Agriculture in the Dry Region of the U.S.S.R., *Economic Geography*, VI (1930), 54-80.

The Ural Mountains

The geological history of the Urals is outlined by ANATOLE SAFONOV: Orogeny of the Urals, *Bulletin* American Association of Petroleum Geologists, XXI (1937), 1439-1463. The development of Magnitogorsk is described by JOHN SCOTT in "Behind the Urals," Boston: Houghton (1942); and Magnetic City, Core of Valiant Russia's Industrial Might, *National Geographic Magazine*, LXXXIII (1943), 525-556.

8. REGIONS OF SOVIET MIDDLE ASIA

In addition to general references such as MIKHAILOV, D'ALMEIDA, and BERG, suggestive material will be found in LIONEL W. LYDE: "The Continent of Asia," London: Macmillan (1933). One of the best sources is the volume by A. WOEIKOF of St. Petersburg entitled "Le Turkestan Russe," Paris (1914).

Suggested Readings

The best references in German are ARVED SCHULTZ: "Die Naturlichen Landschaften von Russisch-Turkestan," Hamburg: Friederichsen (1920); and his section in the "Klute Handbuch" on "Russisch Turkestan"; and FRITZ MACHATSCHEK: "Landeskunde von Russisch Turkistan," Stuttgart (1921).

Caucasia

Two excellently illustrated articles dealing with modern conditions are those by JOHN LEHMAN: Change in the Caucasus, *Geographical Magazine*, II (1935), 125-141; and JOHN R. JENKINS: Climbing in the Caucasus, *Geographical Magazine*, VII (1938), 55-72. One of the excellent series of botanical studies by WILLIAM SEIFRIZ is entitled Vegetation Zones in the Caucasus, *Geographical Review*, XXVI (1936), 59-66. The history of political complications is considered by WILLIAM O. FIELD, JR.: The International Struggle for Transcaucasia, *American Quarterly on the Soviet Union*, II (1939), 21-44. A journey in 1925 is described by FRIDTJOF NANSEN: "Through the Caucasus to the Volga," New York: Norton (1931). The "Klute Handbuch" has a section on "Die Kaukasuslander" by BRUNO PLAETSCHKE; and *Petermann's Mitteilungen*, Erganzungsheft 189 (1926), is on Transkaukasien by ANTON BÜDEL. ROLF SINGER has written Roaming Russia's Caucasus, *National Geographic Magazine*, LXXXII (1942), 91-121.

Caspian Desert

ELLSWORTH HUNTINGTON reviews the problem of climatic changes in an article entitled Fluctuations in the Caspian Sea, *Bulletin* American Geographical Society, XXXIX (1907), 577-596. The problem of agriculture in the lower Volga is considered briefly by W. C. LOWDERMILK and N. MIROV: Irrigation in the Caspian Lowlands, *Geographical Review*, XXIII (1933), 336-337. Petroleum production northeast of the Caspian is described by C. W. SANDERS: Emba Salt Dome Region, *Bulletin* American Association of Petroleum Geologists, XXIII (1939), 492-516. Conditions in the northeast are pictured by IRVINE C. GARDNER: Observing an Eclipse in Asiatic Russia, *National Geographic Magazine*, LXXI (1937), 179-197.

Pamirs and Associated Ranges

In 1903 the Carnegie Institution sent an expedition to the mountains and deserts of Central Asia under RAPHAEL PUMPELLY, WILLIAM M. DAVIS, and ELLSWORTH HUNTINGTON, whose report is "Explorations in Turkestan," Washington (1905). ELLSWORTH HUNTINGTON has also written The Mountains of Turkestan, *Geographical Journal*, XXV (1905), 22-40, 139-158; and The Mountains and Kibitkas of Tian Shan, *Bulletin* American Geographical Society, XXXVII (1905), 513-530. WILLIAM M. DAVIS has further described his travel in A Summer in Turkestan, *Bulletin* American Geographical Society, XXXVI (1904), 217-218. An expedition under W. RICKMER RICKMERS is described in The Alai-Pamirs in 1913 and 1928, *Geographical Journal*, LXXIV (1929), 209-231. See also M. ROMM, "The Ascent of Mt. Stalin," London: Lawrence and Wishart (1936).

Suggested Readings

Oases of Southern Turan

Geographic conditions in the deserts and oases of Turan are described by ALBRECHT PENCK: Central Asia, *Geographical Journal*, LXXVI (1930), 477-487; and W. RICKMER RICKMERS: "The Duab of Turkestan," London: Cambridge University Press (1913). Agricultural developments are considered by VALENTINE V. TCHIKOFF; The Cotton Empire of the U.S.S.R., *Asia*, XXXII (1932), 255-263; LYMAN D. WILBUR: Surveying through Khoresm, *National Geographic Magazine*, LXI (1932), 753-780; and ARTHUR P. DAVIS: Irrigation in Turkestan, *Civil Engineering*, II (1932), 1-5. Other agricultural developments are reported in ROBERT K. NABOURS: The Land of Lambskins, *National Geographic Magazine*, XXXVI (1919), 77-88. Animal life is described by DANIEL KASHKAROV and VICTOR KURBATOV: Preliminary Ecological Survey of the Vertebrate Fauna of the Central Kara-Kum Desert in West Turkestan, *Ecology*, XI (1930), 35-60. Conditions in Kazakhstan are dealt with by ALLAN MOZLEY: The Ponds, Lakes, and Streams of the Kirghiz Steppe, *Scottish Geographical Magazine*, LIII (January, 1937), 1-10. ELIZABETH W. CLARK has written a brief article entitled Golden Samarkand, *Home Geographic Monthly* (November, 1932), 37-42. General travel accounts may be found in BOSWORTH GOLDMAN: "Red Road through Asia," London: Methuen (1934); ELLA K. MAILLART: "Turkestan Solo," New York: Putnam (1935); ELLA R. CHRISTIE: "Through Khiva to Golden Samarkand," London: Seeley Service (1925); and EGON ERWIN KISCH: "Changing Asia," New York: Knopf (1935).

9. REGIONS OF SOVIET SIBERIA

Developments during the first two five-year plans are described in articles by GEORGE B. CRESSEY: News from Siberia, *Harper's Magazine*, CLXXVII (1938), 148-157; and Pioneering in Yeniseiland (incorrectly spelled "Yeneseiland"), *Journal of the Scientific Laboratories*, Denison University, XXIV (1939), 103-169. An earlier account is GEORGE FREDERICK WRIGHT: "Asiatic Russia," New York: McClure, Phillips (1902). BORIS BAIEVSKY has a general article entitled Siberia—The Storehouse of the Future, *Economic Geography*, III (1927), 167-192. Economic developments are covered in numerous short articles in the fortnightly *Far Eastern Survey* published by the INSTITUTE OF PACIFIC RELATIONS. The mineral wealth of Siberia is described by P. P. GOUDKOFF: Economic Geography of the Coal Resources of Asiatic Russia, *Geographical Review*, XIII (1923), 283-293. Conditions under czarist rule are described by GEORGE KENNAN in Siberia—The Exiles' Abode, *Journal* American Geographical Society, XIV (1882), 13-68.

The most extensive bibliography of eastern Siberia is that by ROBERT J. KERNER, entitled "Northeastern Asia, A Selected Bibliography," Berkeley: University of California Press (1939), two volumes.

Standard German sources are ARVED SCHULTZ: "Sibirien," Breslau: Ferdinand Hirt (1923); ERICH THIEL: "Verkehrsgeographie von Russisch-Asien," Berlin: Ost-Europa-verlag (1934); and HELMUT ANGER: "Sibirien" in the "Klute Handbuch."

Suggested Readings

Three volumes that describe Siberia just prior to the Second World War are R. A. DAVIES and ANDREW J. STEIGER: "Soviet Asia," New York: Dial Press (1942); EMIL LENGYEL: "Siberia," New York: Random House (1943); and ERNEST S. BATES: "Soviet Asia," London: J. Cape (1942).

OWEN LATTIMORE has described conditions in eastern Siberia and Middle Asia as seen during an airplane trip from Alaska to China in New Road to Asia, *National Geographic Magazine*, LXXXVI (1944), 641-676.

Yenisei Taiga

FRIDTJOF NANSEN's trip up the Yenisei in 1913 is described in "Through Siberia, The Land of the Future," London: Heinemann (1914). Volumes by modern travelers are BOSWORTH GOLDMAN: "Red Road through Asia," London: Methuen (1934); H. P. SMOLKA: "Forty Thousand against the Arctic," London: Hutchinson (1937); and RUTH GRUBER: "I Went to the Soviet Arctic," New York: Simon & Schuster (1939). A detailed study of the entire Yenisei Valley is presented by GEORGE B. CRESSEY in Pioneering in Yeniseiland. Life among the Nentsi is described by H. U. HALL: A Siberian Wilderness: Native Life on the Lower Yenisei, *Geographical Review*, V (1918), 1-21. A trip to Igarka and up the Yenisei is described by BOSWORTH GOLDMAN: The Arctic Gateway to Siberia, *Geographical Magazine*, II (1936), 231-245; and a brief description of a trip down the Yenisei is provided by A. J. STEIGER: The Mighty Yenesei, *Asia*, XXXVII (1937), 510-513.

Arctic Fringe

In addition to "Forty Thousand against the Arctic," H. P. SMOLKA has written two other studies entitled The Economic Development of the Soviet Arctic, *Geographical Journal*, LXXXIX (1937), 327-343; and Soviet Strategy in the Arctic, *Foreign Affairs*, XVI (1938), 272-278. RUTH GRUBER's "I Went to the Soviet Arctic" contains extensive travel information. Another travel volume is LEONARD MATTERS: "Through the Kara Sea," Sheffington (1932). The U.S.S.R. COUNCIL OF THE INSTITUTE OF PACIFIC RELATIONS has published a report by SEMION JOFFE entitled "The Northern Sea Route as a Transport Problem" (1936). The Soviet Conquest of the Far North is the title of an article by BRUCE HOPPER in *Foreign Affairs*, XIV (1936), 499-505. Abstracts of papers presented at the Seventeenth International Geological Congress on the Geology of Arctic Regions of Eurasia are reprinted in the *Pan-American Geologist*, LXXII (1939), 273-292. Included in WEIGERT and STEFANSSON's "Compass of the World," New York: Macmillan (1944), is an article by ERNEST C. ROPES entitled The Soviet Arctic and the Future.

Lena Taiga

The most recent account of the Lena Valley will be found in RUTH GRUBER's "I Went to the Soviet Arctic." Conditions among the native tribes are described by WALDEMAR JOCHELSON: The Yakut, *Anthropological Papers* American Museum of Natural History, XXXIII (1933), 35-225.

Suggested Readings

Northeastern Mountains

The discovery of the Cherski Range is described by SERGEI OBRUCHEV: Discovery of a Great Range in Northeast Siberia, *Geographical Journal*, LXX (1927), 464-470. N. KRIJANOVSKY has listed the Volcanoes of Kamchatka in the *Bulletin* Geological Society of America, XLV (1934), 529-549. Problems of fishing in the northwestern Pacific are covered in two articles by STANISLAUS NOVAKOVSKY: Geographic Regions of the Fisheries in Asiatic Russia, *Journal of Geography*, XXII (1932), 1-15; and by BORIS BAIEVSKY: Fisheries of Siberia, U. S. Bureau of Fisheries *Document* 1006 (1926), 37-64.

The Far East

Three reports by the U.S.S.R. COUNCIL OF THE INSTITUTE OF PACIFIC RELATIONS in 1936 provide a comprehensive picture of the Amur Basin: "Nature and Natural Resources of the Soviet Far East"; A. TSYMEK: "The Forest Wealth of the Soviet Far East and Its Exploitation"; and E. RAIKHMAN and B. VVEDENSKY: "The Economic Development of the Soviet Far East." STANISLAUS NOVAKOVSKY has written three articles on climatic conditions: Climatic Provinces of the Russian Far East in Relation to Human Activities, *Geographical Review*, XII (1922), 100-115; The Probable Effect of the Climate of the Russian Far East on Human Life and Activity, *Ecology*, III (1922), 181-201; and The Effect of Climate on the Efficiency of the People of the Russian Far East, *Ecology*, III (1922), 275-283. FRIDTJOF NANSEN: "Through Siberia, The Land of the Future," describes conditions in 1913. Material on Sakhalin includes articles by H. R. FRIIS: Pioneer Economy of Sakhalin Island, *Economic Geography*, XV (1939), 55-79; GIICHIRO KOBAYASHI: Preliminary Report on the Geology of the Oil Fields in North Sakhalin, *Bulletin* American Association of Petroleum Geologists, X (1926), 1150-1162; and I. P. TOLMACHOFF: The Results of Oil Prospecting on Sakhalin Island by Japan in 1919-25, *Bulletin* American Association of Petroleum Geologists, X (1926), 1163-1170. A comprehensive analysis of economic and cultural developments is provided in WILLIAM MANDEL: "Soviet Far East and Central Asia," New York: Dial Press (1944).

10. GEOSTRATEGY AND THE FUTURE OF THE UNION

HALFORD J. MACKINDER presents the basic problems of land power versus sea power in his "Democratic Ideals and Reality," New York: Holt (1919). HANS WEIGERT and VILHJALMUR STEFANSSON's symposium "Compass of the World," New York: Macmillan (1944), is the best single collection of essays on geopolitics. ROBERT J. KERNER has traced the evolution of Russian history in terms of geographical influences in his "The Urge to the Sea," Berkeley and Los Angeles: University of California Press (1942). Two excellent articles are found in *Foreign Affairs*, XX (1942), Haushofer and the Pacific by HANS W. WEIGERT, 732-742; and XXI (1943); and The Round World and the Winning of the Peace by HALFORD J. MACKINDER, 595-605. GEORGE B. CRESSEY's Siberia's Role in Soviet Strategy, *Journal of Geography*, XLI (1942), 81-88, has been reprinted in WEIGERT and STEFANSSON's "Compass of the World."

INDEX

Index

Apricots, Oases of Southern Turan, 198, 199
  Pamir Mountains, 193
Apsheron Peninsula, oil, 114-115, 188
Arab culture, Oases of Southern Turan, 199
Arab people, 26, 54
Arabia, 33, 38
Aral Sea, 37, 86, 180, 190
  nature of, 201
  rivers to, 34
  soil, 107
Aral-Balkhash Desert, 84-85, 194, 200-202, 225
  agriculture and trade, 202
  cities, 202
  climate, 200
  geographic structure, 201
  industry and mineral resources, 202
  people, 202
  rivers, lakes, and navigation, 200-201
  soil and vegetation, 201
Ararat, Mt., 187
Arbat, 56
Arctic Circle, 70, 93, 94, 101, 168, 207, 214, 226
  agriculture, 139, 141
  climate, 36, 38-39, 139
  industrial development, 167
  mineral resources, 112, 122
  population, 48
  railways, 135
  settlements in, 216
  tundra, 99
Arctic coast, 34, 97, 166, 238
Arctic Fringe, 84-85, 216-220
  agriculture, 219
  climate and vegetation, 220
  development of, 220
  freight and trade, 217-219
  history, explorations, and Soviet activities, 217
  hunting, fishing, and trapping, 219
  population, education, and racial composition, 219
  ports and seas, 159, 218
Arctic nomads, 173
Arctic Ocean, 3, 71, 95, 134, 224, 240, 243
  climate, 96
  navigation, 3, 137
  weather influence, 36
Arkhangelsk, 214, 217-219
  climate, 97, 169
  population and industry, 17, 170
Armenian Mountains, 32
Armenian people, 26, 43, 52, 61, 186
Armenian Plateau, 91, 186
Armenian Soviet Socialist Republic, 13, 16, 44, 68, 186, 189
Arsenic, Baikalia, 221
  Caucasus, 189

Arsenic, Oases of Southern Turan, 199
Artem, 113
Aryan language, 41
Asbest, 123
Asbestos, 143
  Altai-Sayan, 123
  Ural Mountains, 124, 179, 181
Ashkhabad, 16, 17, 202
Asia, name defined, 30
Asia Minor, 50
Asiatic peoples of the Soviet, 64-66
Assyrian people, 185
Astrakhan, population and industry, 17, 132, 142, 191-192
Astrakhan delta, 136
Assami people, 26
Atlantic Ocean, 139, 159, 167, 240, 241
  climatic weather influence, 36, 96, 149
Atlantic peninsulas, 29, 31
Attila, 49, 52
Australia, trade, 228
Automobiles, 10, 137, 143
  Central Agricultural Region, 171, 177
Autonomous Volga German Republic, 63
Avar people, 26
Aviation, 239
Azerbaidzhanian Soviet Socialist Repub-
Azerbaijani people, 26, 43, 186
  lic, 13, 16, 44, 64, 186
  oil, 114-115
  population and industry, 189
Azov Sea, 51, 57, 69, 91, 174-175
  industry, 127
  fishing, 132, 155
  temperature, 96
Azov-Podolian Shield, 69

B

Baikal Lake, 29, 32-33, 36, 37, 44, 46, 47, 64, 70, 90, 92, 94, 95, 207-208, 213-215, 222
  agriculture, 139
  climate, 98
  iron and steel, 129
  minerals, 119, 122
  mountains, 71
  nature of, 220-222
  railways, 135
  vegetation, 101
  water power, 116-117
Baikal Mountains, 71, 88, 93, 206
Baikal-Amur Railway, 135, 223, 228
Baikalia, 84-85, 220-222
  climate and vegetation, 221
  geography of, 221
  industries, 221-222
  mineral resources, 221
  railways, 222
Baikal-Stanovoi Highlands, 88, 93
Bakal, 128
Baku, 16, 45, 186-187, 189, 251

Index

Index

Index

Georgia, agriculture, 142, 188
  Jewish people, 62
  mineral resources, 114, 120
  [*See also* Georgian (Gruzian) Soviet
    Socialist Republic]
Georgian Military Highway, 189
Georgian people, 12, 26, 43, 52, 61, 62,
  186
Georgian (Gruzian) Soviet Socialist Re-
  public, 13, 15, 16, 44, 186, 189
Geostrategy, as applied to the Soviet
  Union, 237-246
  definition, 237
  elements of, 237-244
German geopolitics, 234-235
German invasion of 1941, 66, 111, 127,
  130, 147, 153, 156, 179
German Knights, 63
German people, 42, 43, 49, 52, 60, 63
Germanic tribes, 58
Germany, 49, 54, 56, 57, 157, 239, 241
  environmental conditions, 146
  industry resources, 110, 123, 126, 151
  trade, 215
Gibraltar, 242
Gilyak people, 26
Gissar Mountains, 92
Glaciers, 71, 86
  Altai Mountains, 208
  Trans-Alai range, 193
Glass, Ukraine, 152
Goats, 172
Gobi Desert, 238
Gold, 10, 78-79, 108, 121, 143, 243, 251
  Aldan Shield, 70
  Altai-Sayan, 207, 211
  Baikalia, 221
  Lena Taiga, 222
  Northeastern Mountains, 226
  Oases of Southern Turan, 199
  Ural Mountains, 124, 179, 181
Gold people, 26
Golden Horde, 5, 56
Goldi people, 26
Golodnaya Steppe, 201
Gomel, 17
Gorki, 15, 45, 174-175
  industry, 130-132, 137, 171
  population, 17, 171
  railways, 135
  wheat, 141
Gorlovka, 17
Gornaya Shoria Mountains, minerals,
  119, 129, 152, 211
Goth people, 49, 51, 53
Gothland Island, 51
Government structure, 16
Grain crops, 10, 136, 140-142, 150, 157,
  177, 202
  (*See also* crops listed separately)
Grapes, 142
  Caucasus, 188

Grapes, Oases of Southern Turan, 198-199
  Pamir Mountains, 193
Graphite, Yenisei Taiga, 215
Grasslands, 39, 100, 103-104, 106
  Altai-Sayan, 209
  Lena Taiga, 224
  Southern Agricultural Region, 177
Great Britain, 7
  English industries, 110, 126, 151
  politics, 235, 242
  trade, 168, 215
Great Khingan Mountains, 227
Great Plains, coal, 110
Great Russian language, 44
Great Russian people, 15, 17, 26, 43, 54,
  64, 67, 172
  religion, 160
Great Soviet World Atlas, 11, 132
Greater-Russia, 58
Greeks, 43, 48, 49, 53, 153, 186
Growing season, short, 95, 139
Grozny, industry, 133
  oil, 114-115, 189
  population, 17
Gruzins (*see* Georgians)
Gujarat people, 26
Gurev, 191
Gydan Peninsula, 88
Gydan Range, 94
Gydan River, 93
Gypsies, 68

H

Handicrafts, 251
  Central Agricultural Region, 172
  Oases of Southern Turan, 199
Hanseatic League, 162
Harvesters and combines, 130, 141
Haushofer, Prof. Karl, 235, 236
Hay, Dvina-Pechora Taiga, 170
  Kola-Karelian Taiga, 168
  Lena Taiga, 224
Heartland concept, 231-238, 241, 245
  defined, 232
Heavy industry, 9, 127-130
  (*See also* Industry; and regions
    listed separately)
Hebrew people, 26, 43
  (*See also* Jewish people)
Hemp, Dvina-Pechora Taiga, 170
  Ukraine, 150
  White Russia, 157
Hermitage Museum, 164
Herodotus, 49, 53
Highways, 137-138, 175
Himalaya, The, 33, 35, 36, 39, 243
Hindu Kush Mountains, 33, 70, 238
Hindustani people, 26
Hitler, Adolf, 235-236, 247
Holland, 215, 238

Index

Index

Lena Taiga, 84-85, 206, 222-225
  agriculture, 224
  climate and vegetation, 223-224
  industries, 222, 224
Lena Valley, 93, 220, 222, 224
  coal, 113
  railways, 135
Lenaland wilderness, 238
Lenin, Mt., 92, 192
Lenin, Nikolay, 6, 116, 125
Leninabad, 196
Leningrad, 2, 14, 17, 45, 98, 134-136, 138,
    171, 175, 242, 247
  (See also Metropolitan Leningrad)
Leninsk-Kuznets, coal, 211
Lesser Caucasus Mountains, 87, 91, 186-
    187
Lett people (see Latvian people)
Libau, 159
Light industry, 131-132
Lignite, 110, 112
  Central Agricultural Region, 177
  Urals, 180
Limestone, Armenia, 132
  Baltic States, 160
  Ukraine, 151
Lin Yu-tang, 235
Linen-weaving, 131
Linseed oil, Baltic states, 161
Lipetsk, iron and steel, 118, 128
Lithuania, 5, 48, 62, 143, 158
Lithuanian people, 26, 58-59, 147
Lithuanian Soviet Socialist Republic, 14
Little Khingan Mountains, 119, 129, 227,
    229
Little Russia (see Ukrainia)
Little Russian people, 15, 43, 54
  (See also Ukrainian people)
Livestock, 178, 248
  Aral-Balkhash, 202
  Yenisei Taiga, 216
Livonia, 68
Livonian people, 59
Locomotives, 112, 130, 154
Loess, 149, 197
Loessial soil, 103
Lower Cretaceous, oil, 115
Lower Dnieper Plain, 87, 91
Lower Tanguska River (see Nizhni River)
Lugansk (see Voroshilovgrad)
Lumber, 10, 131
  Central Agricultural Region, 172, 177
  Leningrad, 164
  White Russia, 157
  Yenisei Taiga, 216
  (See also Timber)
Luoravetlan people, 26
Luri people, 26
Lwow, 15

M

Machine tools, 143, 154, 177
Machine tractor stations, 141
Machinery, 130, 132, 143, 153
  American, 248
  Central Agricultural Region, 177
  Leningrad, 163
  Ukraine, 152, 155, 180
Mackinder, Sir Halford J., 231-233, 236,
    238, 241, 244
Magadan, 137, 226
Magnesite, Sverdlovsk, 123
Magnesium salts, Ural Mountains, 122-
    125, 179, 181
Magnet Mountain, 128
Magnetite, 119
  Altai-Sayan, 211
  Kola-Karelia, 167
Magnitogorsk, 126, 182
  industry, 11, 113, 128, 130, 133, 180,
    212
  mineral resources, 117, 118, 127, 183
  population, 17
  railways, 135
Maikop, oil, 114, 115, 189
  population, 17
Makeevka, blast furnaces, 127-128, 151,
    155
Makeyevka, population, 17
Makhach-Kala, 17
Maklakova, 215
Makran Mountains, 33
Malachite, 123
Malayan people, 26
Manchuria, 7, 222, 227, 228, 242
  railways, 135
  temperature, 38
Manganese, 10, 78-79, 119-120, 127, 143,
    251
  Altai-Sayan, 207, 210, 211
  Caucasus, 124, 189
  Ukraine, 70, 123, 151
  Ural Mountains, 179, 181, 183
Manych River, 91
Maratha people, 26
Marco Polo, 193
Mari, 195, 200
Mariinsk, coal, 113
Mariinsk Canal, 136, 162
Mariitsi people, 43
Maritime Europe, 232
Maritime Province, lead and zinc, 120
Maritime territory, 226
Mariupol, coal, 127
  industry, 133, 152, 155
  population, 17
Marshes, 101, 139, 140
  (See also Swamps; regions listed
    separately)
Matochkin Strait, 218

Index

N

O

Index

Index

Index

Index